Journey to the Middle Kingdom

中国游记

CHRISTOPHER WEST

SIMON & SCHUSTER

LONDON·SYDNEY·NEW YORK·TOKYO·SINGAPORE·TORONTO

First published in Great Britain by
Simon & Schuster Ltd in 1991
A Paramount Communications Company

Copyright © Christopher West, 1991

Simon & Schuster Ltd
West Garden Place
Kendal Street
London W2 2AQ

Simon & Schuster of Australia Pty Ltd
Sydney

A CIP catalogue record for this book is
available from the British Library
ISBN 0–671–71043–5

Typeset in Garamond 11/13 by Falcon Typographic Art Ltd
Edinburgh & London
Printed and bound in Great Britain by
Butler & Tanner Ltd, Frome

For Tara

CONTENTS

旅

ACKNOWLEDGEMENTS

Many individuals have helped with this book. Particular thanks must go to Tara Gulati, who paid a high price for my obsession with its creation; to my parents, for their often bewildered but never flagging support; to Nigel Kotani and Clare Goldrick, for their detailed travellers' expertise and simple travellers' enthusiasm; to Meme and YJ, for their knowledge and love of China; to Clare Dymond, Rivers Scott and Maureen Waller. But you, the reader, should have some thanks too – and the people I met on my journey: all of them, good and bad, Chinese and Western.

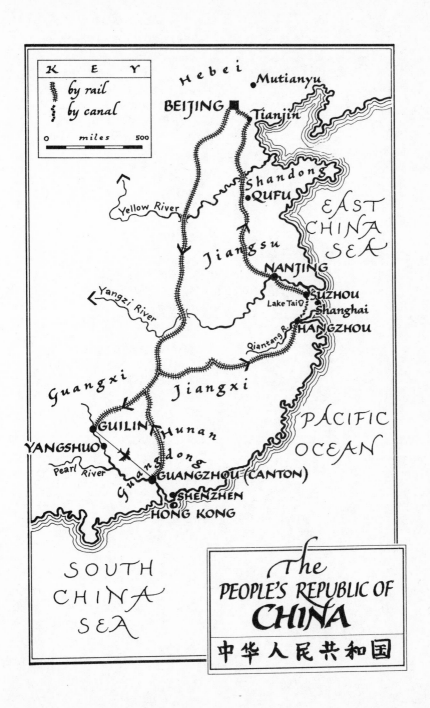

Hebei

• Mutianyu

BEIJING ■

Tianjin

Shandong

• QUFU

EAST
CHINA
SEA

Yellow River

Jiangsu

Yangzi River

NANJING

SUZHOU

Lake Tai

Shanghai

HANGZHOU

Qiantang R.

Guangxi

Jiangxi

PACIFIC
OCEAN

GUILIN

Hunan

YANGSHUO•

Guangdong

Pearl River

GUANGZHOU (CANTON)

SHENZHEN

HONG KONG

SOUTH
CHINA
SEA

The
PEOPLE'S REPUBLIC OF
CHINA
中华人民共和国

1

Out with the Pack

I sank into the flood of shouting, jostling passengers with a feeling of relief – no more doubts were possible: I was going, whether I wanted to or not. The border was less than a hundred yards ahead now, visible through the still, green palm-fronds with its tin customs sheds, barbed wire and bandy-legged watch towers. A mile beyond them, the hills of Shenzhen, People's Republic of China, shimmered in the heat. I was about to become a traveller.

At the far end of the walkway, a sign bid us WELCOME! A line of soldiers stood beneath it, expressionless, their bayonets fixed and ready for use.

ALIENS THIS WAY. A second notice siphoned us few Westerners off to a large hall, where customs officials – in the same jungle green as the border guards – sat behind desks, staring and whispering. A queue snaked back from the one open position.

'Next!' The passport officer's voice echoed round the steel ribs of the ceiling, and we shuffled forward a place. To soothe a sudden attack of nerves, I began rehearsing some of the phrases I had been studying with naive eagerness since deciding to make this journey. *At the border. Here is my vaccination certificate. Here is my currency declaration. This visa is valid for three months.* (Get those tones right! Mandarin has four, each of which gives a word a totally different meaning.)

'Next!'

I have no firearms, explosives or pornographic material.

'Next!'
I have no literature of a politically subversive nature.
'Next!'
I have no –
'Next!'
He meant me.
'Er, *ni hao*,' I replied. 'Hello' – the one word every visitor learns before setting off. The officer winced as if I had cracked a weak joke, then grabbed my passport and began scribbling on it.
'How long are you staying for?'
'Two months.'
He gave me a long, searching stare. 'Why?'
Adventure, excitement, education; to visit the country most different from my own that I could imagine; to make my mind up about Marxism, about nature and nurture, about East and West; to still the restlessness I felt when I contemplated my life.
'Holiday,' I said in English.
He nodded and handed back my papers.
'Next!'

Shenzhen station was another tin hut, painted black to attract maximum heat and crammed beyond bursting point with people. It was damper and hotter than any place I had ever been; it stank of diesel fuel, drains, urine and sweat; it reverberated to the din of shouting and spitting. A tannoy overhead yapped a series of metallic moon-language instructions – a few individuals stopped to listen, nodding as they took in the information, the rest barged on unheeding; they knew all they needed to know, anyway. Alone in my continuing ignorance, I scanned the walls for any sign not in Chinese characters.
'Excuse me, where is the booking office?' Although I had practised the phrase a hundred times, I still glanced down at the phrase book wobbling in my hand. Even then, the first person I asked simply ignored me, while the second grabbed the book and began reading it to his friends.
'This is left luggage,' said the clerk at the nearest desk.
'Yes, I can see that. But *where* is the booking office?'

'*Meiyou,*' he replied. 'No' – the one word every visitor learns once in China.

I glared at him.

'You have luggage?' he continued.

'No.'

He pointed at my pack.

'Yes.'

'You can leave it here. All day. Ten fen.'

'I want a ticket,' I said.

He started to write.

'For a train. To Guangzhou. The first one possible.'

'Ah! Then you need the booking office. This is left luggage.' He ripped my 'ticket' up and turned away contemptuously.

'*Kai wang xi'an de Lieche* . . .!' the tannoy shrieked.

I finally found the right window and joined another queue. Each ticket seemed to take an age to make out. After about half an hour I was near the front, and getting nervous. Then the clerk slammed a wooden barrier across his face.

'*Xiuxi* [siesta],' the man in front of me explained. 'Guangzhou? Try that window over there.'

When eventually I was served, the vendor burst out laughing at my pronunciation. Those tones – what had I said? 'Please banana me a tadpole to Guangzhou'?

Clutching my piece of paper, I staggered out of the entrance and collapsed on the steps, desperate for air, coolness and self-respect. Was nothing going to be easy in the next two months? Finding accommodation, finding food, getting from any one place to another. My head began to spin, my body to sweat in a sudden, irrational panic.

'Serves me right!' I muttered, as a man in a Mao suit subjected me to a long, piercing stare, then spat on the pavement. I hadn't been brave and clever to come to this place, but arrogant and stupid. I was ignorant, ill-prepared, frightened and alone.

Looking back, there couldn't have been a better frame of mind in which to start travelling.

The seats filled up as eleven thirty approached. Four men across the carriage aisle produced an icebox and flipped open their beer bottles with a hiss that made me wince with thirst. A vendor wheeled a trolley of jangling soft drinks past the window; I was about to shout out to him, but didn't. Choosing, asking, paying (half the notes I'd got from the People's Bank had no Western numerals on) – it all seemed too much effort.

Well, you're on the right train! I told myself (it had the destination in Western letters on the side of the carriage). An achievement like this called for celebration – a square of chocolate from the bar I had bought at Kowloon station. I opened my pack and dug it out. It had melted all over my Mandarin dictionary. I was marshalling the foulest expletives at my command – who'd mind? who'd understand? – when I heard a European voice close by.

'Hello. My seat, I think.' The speaker was a small, curly-haired woman of about thirty. She was pointing at the place right opposite me.

'What? There? Why, that's marvellous!'

She gave a shrug and and swung her pack up on the rack with expert ease. 'It's usual. They like to put the foreigners together.'

'How thoughtful of them.'

'It's a relic of the Seventies, when Chinese weren't allowed to mix with us at all.'

She sat down and introduced herself as Marie-Claude. She was thin and plain, her clothes simple and tatty: a pink batik T-shirt, a billowing skirt of rough green cloth, leather chappals. Her skin had been tanned dark brown, but not in a glitzy St Tropez way – it was dry and uncared-for. But her eyes shone with enthusiasm and confidence.

'You have just arrived?' she asked.

'Is it that obvious?' I replied.

'Yes – but that's nothing to be ashamed of. All that learning to do! You're so lucky!'

'Yes . . .'

At half past on the dot, the train gave a jolt and we were on our way to Guangzhou. We rolled slowly through the centre of Shenzhen Special Economic Zone, with its luxury hotels, offices and motorways, then into the suburbs, where tower blocks signalled whole novels in washing. It seemed no different to the world I had left behind the border.

It held no interest for my companion. 'You have your mug?' she said.

'Mug?'

'Everyone on Chinese trains carries a mug.'

'What for?'

'Tea, of course.' She produced a khaki canvas bag that looked even more travel-battered than she did, and began rummaging in it. After a minute or so, she found a Tupperware container of dried jasmine leaves; at exactly the same moment, a uniformed attendant appeared at the end of the corridor, pushing a samovar on a trolley. He made his way slowly up the aisle, serving us just as Marie-Claude dug me out a paper cup, formerly 'Property of Singapore Airport'.

'*Ganbei* [cheers]!' she said, once we had been served. 'To your journey! May it enrich your spirit – if that is what you wish.'

'Thanks. Er, *ganbei*!'

I took a sip and swallowed a mouthful of leaves. We looked at each other and burst out laughing.

The Special Economic Zone soon gave way to dirt tracks and thatched stone farmsteads, then to heath, boulders and stunted trees – an ugly, cruel landscape, where nobody lived and nothing useful grew. The only human activity was a gang of straw-hatted navvies hacking at the bare, red rock with wooden hoes. Their legs and torsos glistened with sweat; their backs were burnt brown: it looked dreadful work, in dreadful conditions, though when I tried to study their faces, I could see no expression at all. Just like the border guards, they seemed to be men without feelings, a new super-race of helots for a new world of absolute drabness.

But these impressions did not last. The hills disappeared and the train rumbled out on to a wide, sunlit plain, where colourful paddy fields welcomed us from between winding, irregular mudbanks, brimming with rice at every stage of cultivation: black needles, just breaking the shimmering water; thick turquoise mats ready for harvest; half-grown shoots of a gorgeous, celebratory spring green. In many of them, men and women stood calf-deep, planting, weeding or gathering. Their work looked almost as tough as the road-builders' – foot-rotting and back-breaking – but whenever a straw hat turned and lifted to watch the train go by, it revealed a universally comprehensible grin.

My confusion changed from 'what?' to 'why?' Were these people smiling because their surroundings were so lovely? Because they worked at their own, untroubled pace? (Look at them, swaying through their tasks with the grace of athletes.) Was it because they were becoming rich under the new 'responsibility system'? Or because they were still poor? We passed another ramshackle village of mud paths, stepped gables and twirling roof corners; we crossed a highway as straight as an arrow, with a chubby truck bouncing into the distance, followed by a fox tail of dust. China's countryside looked unimaginably remote, especially to me with my nervous beginner's Mandarin and my visa for 'open cities' only – but the sight of it filled me with an extraordinary joy.

Marie-Claude was reading *Wisdom of the Zen Masters*. I had been staring out at Guangdong province for ages, entranced by its beauty in a way I hadn't been since childhood. But I should talk to my companion.

'You've been on the road a while, then?'

'Yes,' she replied.

'Tell me about it.'

'It's wonderful.'

'In what way?'

'Lots of ways . . .' She eyed me suspiciously. Was I someone in whom she could confide? We thundered on to a girder bridge, over a shining river full of barges and fishing boats. My heart leapt at the sight, and maybe that showed.

'I've been travelling for years,' she began, lowering her book. 'I went to India as soon as I left school. Everyone said I was crazy. I knew I was right, the moment I arrived. I couldn't say why, I just knew. I could feel it in the noise, the heat, the crowds. Such humanity, such excitement!'

I nodded. Not quite my experience of Shenzhen, but still . . .

'I'd spent nineteen years "growing up",' she continued. 'Nineteen years learning how to be sensible, calculating and worldly, how to smother reactions and feelings that didn't fit what I was supposed to be. But the moment the plane door opened, I knew that all those years had been wasted, that I had to start all over again. From there, from then. It was instant enlightenment.'

As we rolled across the rice fields, Marie-Claude gave me an account of her new 'enlightened' life – a chronicle of beaches, temples and cities, of mountain treks and slow, magical, comfortless train rides. Three years – she had planned to stay six months.

'I left India only because I had to. My mother was ill, and nobody else could look after her. My brothers were all too busy with their careers. I was happy to do that, but when she got better, I made my mistake. I stayed behind in the West. I let everyone convince me that I'd "got over" travelling, that I had to get on with "real" life. I still kept studying Buddhism – though they tried talking me out of that, too – but I found a job, rented a flat, all that kind of thing. Of course, it drove me mad – but I'd fallen back into thinking that was because there was something wrong with me. Everyone else was happy saving for bigger cars or luxury holidays: I was – well, odd. One day, I was walking past a travel agent, and I saw a picture of the Potala Palace in Lhasa. I could feel my heart pounding, and sinking, too – like falling in love. Oh, no – not again . . . Next day I just went out and bought a one-way ticket.

'I've been all over Asia since then. I go back to France occasionally, to see my family and get some money together, but it seems stranger every time. This is where I belong: on the road.'

She smiled proudly and began burrowing in that bag again. I looked away to hide the scepticism that had crept into my mind. In her own eyes, Marie-Claude might belong here – but in the eyes of the Chinese, of people who did not have the option of crossing that barbed-wire barrier? I wondered if I hadn't met my first travel junkie – a misfit in her own society, artificially secure in somebody else's. Then I looked out at those bright-green fields again, at those dignified men and women . . .

'Chocolate?' she asked.

'Thanks.' Panda brand.

'It's not as nice as the Western stuff, but it stands the heat better.' She laughed. 'You wouldn't believe how many travellers arrive in Guangzhou, open their rucksacks and find that the little treat they brought over from Hong Kong has melted all over their books and clothing.'

'No . . .'

This chocolate dissolved into lumps in my mouth. It tasted of dry nothingness, like sawdust or tiny pieces of hardened sponge.

'You have studied Zen?' she went on, after a pause.

'Er, a little. There's never enough time to do all the things you want to, is there?'

'But you're familiar with these wonderful riddles? *The Koans of Wei Lang?*'

'Well . . .'

'I used to read them to my colleagues at work. Imagine it! *A pupil once asked the master: 'How do I find enlightenment?' He replied: 'What is this "I"?' – and the pupil knew Zen.* They didn't understand, of course. They didn't even try.'

I ought to try, anyhow.

'What is this I? What is this I?' I imagined the train wheels rattling. A man? An Englishman? A failed musician now publishing other people's work? Then I looked out of the window at a girl with a pink umbrella driving a water buffalo about twenty times her size along a mudbank. Hell, the question could wait.

There had been no shadows for most of the trip, but now they were creeping out from under the palm groves and houses, hollowing the rice paddies and digging ruts in the dirt tracks. The shabby brick towns were growing larger and more frequent, acquiring concrete blocks and macadamed roads: countryside was being replaced by city – the world to which we passers-by really belonged.

'Is this Guangzhou already?' I asked, my heart sinking.

'It's half past four,' said Marie-Claude.

So soon?

My friend began packing her bag, then stood up. 'You must excuse me,' she went on. 'The airline office closes at five.'

'Airline?' It hardly suited her style.

'There's no other way of getting to Tibet.'

She flipped her rucksack down from the rack and on to her

back in one unthinking, Zen-master movement, then barged out into the queue that had already formed in the aisle.

'*Au revoir!*'

'*Au revoir.*'

Platform 3 flash-flooded as soon as we pulled in, and my companion was swept out of view. After a sentimental twinge of loss, I shrugged – on the road I'd have to get used to short-lived relationships with people and with places. Goodbye, Marie-Claude; hello, Guangzhou. I tugged at my pack, and it thudded down on the table like lead.

Hello, Guangzhou. Heat blazed down from the cloudless sky and up from the concrete of the forecourt. The crowd of several thousand, with whom I had squeezed past one officious ticket collector, was still surging all round me, a mass of elbows, boots and steel-cornered suitcases. More people thronged up to welcome them. It was like the meeting of two rain-filled rivers; and I was a piece of driftwood bobbing in the middle.

'Sell FEC?' hissed the young man at my shoulder. 'One twenty!' By Western standards of proximity, he was either a close friend or about to attack.

'Sorry?' I replied.

'One two five?'

'I don't understand.'

He turned away, and was replaced at once by an old woman with a bundle of maps.

'You buy?' She jabbed me with one, then unfolded a corner.

'CANTON,' I read.

'Look – English! One yuan!'

I paused, unable to think.

'Ninety fen. Eighty . . .'

'Okay,' I muttered. I gave her what I hoped was a yuan; she stuffed a map and some grubby, numberless notes into my hand. I opened my purchase – apart from the name, it was all in Chinese characters.

'Hey!' But she was gone. Another woman sidled up with the same product.

'You buy? Fifty fen. Look, English!'

*

Hello, Guangzhou. The orderly queue for the Route 5 bus had just dissolved into a free-for-all, leaving me shocked and fearful on the periphery of a human whirlpool.

'Don't worry,' said the man beside me as the vehicle creaked off. 'There's another in half an hour.'

But then I'd have to go through all that again. Between me and Shamian Island (the destination recommended by Marie-Claude), there *had* to be that struggle – those women to be elbowed aside, those ill-shod feet to be stamped on.

'You are from America?' the man continued. He had an easy, unhurried smile, though a minute ago his face had been twisted with furious determination as he fought to get on board the bus.

'No,' I replied. 'England.'

'Ah, England.' He nodded vaguely, as if he had heard of the place somewhere before, then squatted down on his haunches and lit a cigarette. For him, this was everyday life.

Hello, Guangzhou. Renmin Lu – People's Road: the perfect name for the extraordinary, unplanned carnival of activity that had engulfed our bus and brought it to a halt. Round-nosed trams and swaying trolleybuses; red Nissan taxis blaring disco music; buses like this one, so full that their windows looked blacked out. A grey army truck inched past, workmen sitting on the mountain of rubble in the back, laughing and smoking. And a black 1950s-style Hongqi (Red Flag) limousine, its imperial passenger curtained from view ('The instruments of power must not be shown to anyone,' Lao Zi had written). And a policeman in reflector sunglasses and a face mask, on a brand-new blue and white motorcycle with Police Department on the side in Pinyin. In special, chained-off bike lanes, unending schools of heavy, black cycles flowed north and south, jangling their bells and weaving in and out of one another's path like contrapuntal new-age music. Among them, lumbering like whales, were carts piled high with goods and pedalled – or sometimes pulled – by wiry, sweating coolies in shorts and T-shirts. (How would I feel if that were my life?) On the pavements, shoppers crammed round the windows of the big stores, ogling the scooters, colour TVs and cassette players selling for a year's wages. A select few had actually bought: a man in purple flared trousers was dancing with his electric fan; a couple were balancing a tubular steel sofa on their heads. Most had come to dream, and to make their real purchases down Renmin Lu's *hutongs* (side streets), from the stalls festooned with shoulder bags, thermos flasks, buckets, baseball caps and shirts – all goods in deafening day-glo colours, all at negotiable prices.

Bike bells, engines and klaxons; the ting of a trolleybus and the scratch of its pantograph along the heavy overhead wires; the sound of bargaining, arguments, laughter and busy feet: a glorious hubbub arose from this scene, which set my nerves twanging, my head reeling, and my spirits leaping with inexplicable joy.

I lay on my bed and stared up at the mosquito net coiled above me. Through the tattered net curtains floated the voices of two Cantonese arguing: a duet of welcome. I had arrived in their city, in their country; I had found myself a niche of quiet and privacy in their noisy, public world. I rolled over and made myself another cup of tea from the bedside thermos. I lay watching the steam curl towards the cracked ceiling. Here, in Room 105, it could take as long as it liked.

The door flew open with a bang. Marie-Claude strode in.

'Got my ticket!' she exclaimed, chucking her gear down on one of the other beds and grinning. 'Tomorrow, three o'clock!'

'Oh.'

'So let's go!'

'Go?'

She paused. 'Aren't you pleased to see me?'

'Of course. But, well, I'm exhausted. That bus . . .'

'Pfah! You'll get used to that. Finish your tea and we'll go and watch the sunset. You'll hate yourself if you don't.'

She was, of course, right. Shamian glowed in the evening light: the peeling, pastel-stucco colonial mansions where the Taipans had once lived; their gardens of bougainvillea, palm trees and pink-blossoming cherries, now run wild. The cobbled, traffic-free streets were still hot from the day's sun and packed with Chinese visitors: old men sitting on benches, reading papers and smoking; young couples walking hand in hand, glancing at each other with that universal emotion – love. This tumultuous, hyperactive city was at rest, off guard.

'Chang-e money?' whispered a voice from an alleyway.

Marie-Claude tried to explain the black market to me – how the Foreign Exchange Certificates I had received at the border gave the touts access to scarce imported goods; how the *renminbi* I was being offered would buy most of the things a backpack traveller needed; how I should bargain, the way all business was done in the East; how an offer of a hundred and twenty RMB for a hundred FEC was an insult. I nodded, half taking these things in, and we wandered happily into a riverside park (admission, 3 fen, FEC or RMB). At one end, teenagers in dark glasses and platform shoes were playing pool at open-air tables, bragging, missing simple pots, laughing at each other's incompetence. Next to them, a group of old women stood on a lawn, swaying through a routine of *taijiquan* – as graceful as the pool-players were gawky and maladroit. They were the young ones, these septuagenarian ballerinas, defying time with their slow-motion kicks and crouches, their trunk-bends and the sweeping, expansive flings of their wrinkled arms.

'T'ai chi should always be done by water if possible,' said Marie-Claude. Behind the women's flowing bodies, the Pearl River shone purple with the sky. A rusty ferry chugged upstream, cutting a rippling black V across the surface; the waves came lapping up against the embankment, where a classical, dragon-hipped pavilion stood silhouetted against the sunset.

A moment of absolute beauty shocked me with its intensity, then was gone.

My evening ended in the hotel bar, with absurdly romantic names buzzing around my ears: Shanghai, Beijing, Guilin – had these ordinary-looking young people really been to these extraordinary-sounding places? I wanted to stay up all night and eavesdrop, but tiredness insisted otherwise. Back in Room 105, of course, I couldn't sleep – a parade of memories was marching past my eyelids, banners flying. The harshness of the border; the gentle welcome of the rice fields; rush hour on Renmin Lu; old ladies doing t'ai chi by the Pearl River. I had been a traveller only for a day – but if I had to turn round tomorrow, it would still be an experience I would treasure all my life.

2

Views from a Room

Marie-Claude looked across the breakfast table at the guidebook I was annotating. 'If you follow that, you'll just see what every other traveller sees.'

'That's fine by me,' I replied. On her insistence we were eating a Chinese breakfast; sticky rice, pickles, squares of bean curd.

'Well, it shouldn't be.' She shook her head. 'You should make your own discoveries.'

'But I want to see the best places. The most beautiful buildings, the most historical sites . . .'

'Tourism kills them.'

Tourism? It was 1985: China had been open to solo travellers only for a couple of years.

'Take it from me,' she went on. 'If you want to love a place, you must make it your own. And you don't do that wandering round in a group.' She looked earnest, then smiled. 'I've an idea.'

We squeezed ourselves between the motor vehicles on Sun Yat Sen Road, Marie-Claude tinging her bell with delight as we inched past a bus queue psyching itself up to board an approaching 5. A Westerner gazed enviously at us from the back of an immobile taxi – maybe he didn't know that one task at least in this city was easy: hiring bicycles.

'Turn left!' my guide shouted. We swung into an alley, coasting past a line of peasants who squatted on the pavement haggling with townspeople over the fruit and vegetables piled up beside them. These vendors had done their quotas of communal work and were selling produce grown on their own land in their own time, for whatever the buyers would pay. The 'responsibility system' had, apparently, already made some people rich.

At the far end of the road we stopped by a carved stone gateway. Hawkers crowded round us, wrinkled, foul-smelling and aggressive, shoving their gimcrack goods into our faces and hissing through stained, irregular teeth. I was torn between pity and disgust – not everyone was getting rich.

'Ignore them,' said Marie-Claude, barging her way out of their circle. (How callous, I thought; then someone began poking me in the ribs.) 'Lock your bike and follow me.'

The gateway led into a muddy, sloping alley, whose twists and high brick walls slowly shut out the gabbling voices, preparing us for what lay at the end: a temple. A huge brass incense burner stood in the middle of a flagstone courtyard, puffing essence of sandalwood out into the still, receptive air. Round the brightly tiled walls were ramshackle wooden shrines covered in flowers: on one, a candle was burning with a steady, smoke-capped flame. An old man knelt before it in contemplation. His tranquillity was as shocking as the racket of the streets outside.

Marie-Claude pointed at a square wooden building in the far corner. Its orange gambrel roof and overhanging eaves must have been beautiful before the lichen and mildew attacked them. Its columns drooped tatters of crimson paint; the doorway had been shored up with cardboard.

'The great hall,' she said. 'You must see inside.'

I paused. It was so strange, so shabby – just like the hawkers waiting out there. If these people revered it, why had they let it get into this state?

'Come on.'

It was pitch black inside. For a second, panic filled me. I took a long, deep breath to reorient myself. I was here – and this place was real. It had a smell of mildew, smoke and stale incense, a sound of mumbled prayers and shuffling feet, and, as my eyes grew accustomed to the darkness, visible objects – a pinpoint circle of candles and a statue rising out of them, depicting a stooping old man with a long white beard and a hypertrophied egg of a forehead.

'Lao Zi,' Marie-Claude hissed.

'Ah.' Lao Zi, Lao Tzu – the 'Old One', the founder of Taoism; the man who had produced that quote about 'hiding the instruments of government' (from which I had built up an image of *Daojiao* as a sinister, primitive cult – how much I had to learn!).

'You see – religion is still alive in China!' she continued.

Now I could see worshippers in front of the statue, on their knees, heads bowed and hands tightly clasped like medieval penitents. On the end of the line, a woman stared up at the philosopher-god with an expression of appalling anguish. Her lips were quivering as if she were battling against her own words. Had she really done something utterly wicked – or were my immediate intuitions correct, that this was an innocent person in the grip of a mindless, outmoded superstition?

I made for the door and plunged out into the light again.

'How can you love that place?' I said, as we stood by our cycles.

'Didn't you feel the spirituality?'

'Spirituality? All I saw was suffering.'

'Exactly.' Marie-Claude flipped her wheel lock open.

'I don't understand,' I said, after a long fight with mine.

'In the West, we pretend that suffering doesn't exist. In Asia, you have to accept it.'

'I don't see that. Why? Look at the Communists. Whatever you feel about some of their –'

'No!' my companion cut in. 'Suffering is part of the human condition. That's the first principle of Buddhism. The beginning of wisdom. Communism doesn't have any answers to that – any more than capitalism does. They're both far too worldly, too superficial, too materialistic. Far too Western.'

'People in the East are materialistic, too,' I replied uneasily. 'I mean, look at those pavement markets. Those vendors are after every fen they can get, and so are their customers.'

She was ready for this. 'That's not the same. In the East you can be competent in your work and still have room for higher things. Back home, we've squeezed religion right out of the picture. I think it's driven us mad, as a society, as a culture . . .'

We rode off, back down the alley and on to the main road, past the shops stacked high with consumer goods and the crowds which had come to admire them. Neither of us spoke, as if a barrier had come down between us. Traveller versus tourist?

Marie-Claude broke the silence. 'D'you think I'm crazy?'

'Crazy?'

'Yes. Lots of Englishmen think that about anyone who's religious.'

I shook my head.

'What *do* you think, then?'

'I don't know. I just didn't like that temple.'

Another silence.

'I haven't really told you why I go travelling,' Marie-Claude began.

'I thought you had.'

'Not properly. It's not easy. Not everyone with a backpack is what I'd call a traveller, someone who'd understand.'

'Try me and see.'

'Okay. It was my father – he was the one who made me into a traveller . . .'

I smiled, imagining an enlightened old man giving his daughter a rucksack for her eighteenth birthday, and telling her to go out and see the world.

'He died when I was a teenager. In such absolute terror. He tried to hide it from us, of course, but he was never very good at concealment. I've never seen anyone so scared of anything. We all did what we could to help, and I don't feel guilty. But I feel so let down by all those big things that we were supposed to believe in, which were supposed to help us. "Science." That kept him going for a few extra months of pain. "Religion." The church offered him a deal – lie about what you've believed all your life, and you'll be okay. He sent the "holy father" away – quite right, but that made the fear even worse.

'Afterwards, I made a resolution, to find an answer – the one I couldn't give him. I started with Christianity, the only way I knew. But the memory of that smug, scheming priest wouldn't go away. So I tried existentialism – Sartre's *La Nausée*. But I didn't really understand it.' (I nodded in sympathy. At seventeen I had wanted to be Antoine Roquentin, too – aloof, brilliant, taking on the world.) 'Then I found a Hindu guru. Enlightenment for sale. I knew that was wrong – real holy men don't drive round in Rolls-Royces – but I was desperate. When they started asking for money, I tried to leave the ashram. Disciples came knocking on the door in the middle of the night. They threatened to break it down. So much for their spirituality. Asia was my last chance – I really was going crazy. So off I went, to Bombay. You know the rest.

'India's still a religious place, in its heart, despite all the wheeling and dealing you see on the streets. It's a place where a search like mine makes sense, where you can get on with it slowly and purposefully, and not be thought foolish or lazy.

'China's like that, too,' she added, after a pause. 'Forty years of dialectical materialism can't change two and a half thousand years of spirituality.'

Or two and a half thousand years of superstition . . . Back home, I had long ago concluded that religions created more problems than they solved, that they caused bigotry, oppression, repression and economic stagnation. What good had that woman in the temple been doing herself or anyone else?

'So, have you found your answer?' I asked.

'No. But I know it's there, so I don't mind. I can see it in Asian people I meet – not all of them, of course, but enough. And I have moments of Zen awareness that tell me I'm on the right path – you know what I mean.'

The time for pretence was over. 'Not really,' I said.

She smiled. 'You will. I can tell. When you're ready.'

We pulled up at a traffic light, and I gave my companion a searching look. Joy was beaming out of her face in the most contagious manner. I cringed inside at the glib way I had written her off as a no-hoper on the train from Shenzhen, but smiled at the thought that I had her company for a whole morning.

'So,' said Marie-Claude. 'Guangzhou for beginners . . . The Six Banyan Temple: very touristy, but Bodhidharma is supposed to have stayed there. Since when, the site has been free of mosquitoes, so they say. Sun Yat Sen Hall, that's a must.

And Renmin Park, where we'll see the old men with their songbirds. And a yogurt stall – you must try that. Come on! We've a lot to do.'

My head spun from the rising heat of the day and a morning crammed with sights and memories. Marie-Claude glanced at her watch. I felt a stab of pain at her impending departure. How quickly things change!

'One last place,' she said. We turned into Liuersan Lu, the busy embankment road north of the island, and parked by a squat, windowless building. As we walked in, bending to get under the lintel, I heard the sound of spitting. Warnings of Chinese xenophobia sprang into my mind, and I froze.

Marie-Claude laughed. 'You'll have to get used to that in China,' she said.

'Spitting – in restaurants?'

'In restaurants, on the buses, at the opera . . .'

Another expectoration.

'The main thing is not to get paranoid. That's the worst fault a solo traveller can make.'

We found a table. Marie-Claude swept the mess left by the previous occupants to the floor, while I gazed round at the cracked, whitewashed walls and the cobweb-grey ceiling. The customers stared at us, their unashamed, unblinking eyes fixing me as if I were a specimen under a microscope. Someone else spat.

Don't get paranoid. Maybe I should stare back at someone. I scanned the room for a victim: the girl at the cash desk, totting up a bill on an abacus; the waitress, idling in a corner; the cook in the kitchen, his brow glistening red from flames beneath his grease-blackened wok. He'd do. But the longer I looked at him, the more my aggression turned to admiration: it must have been hellishly hot in his cramped workplace – it was bad enough out here – yet he was smiling as he cooked, nodding his head to the beat of a radio and stirring the food with a cheerful flourish. China, land of toil and grins. The people all around me probably had as tough a time at work: if two travellers could brighten their day by accepting a few stares, we should do so with grace.

'Chinese leaf with rice,' said Marie-Claude, when the waitress finally came up to our table. A few more minutes – during which the stares began to subside – and our lunch arrived, steaming and smelling of garlic and shallots.

'*Bon appetit!*'

'Thanks, it looks delicious.'

'Of course. What were you expecting?'

I began to eat, pincering a small leaf, raising it to my lips and delicately nibbling it, proud of my carefully practised mastery of chopsticks. Marie-Claude burst out laughing again.

'What's funny?'

'Your eating. Look around you.'

The Chinese slouched over the tables, the bowls held right under their chins, from where they shovelled the food into their mouths, slurping and sucking with unfettered relish.

'I don't think I could ever be happy in the West now,' she went on, digging in Cantonese-style, still laughing as she did so. Of all my memories of my first fellow traveller, that one is my favourite.

The airport bus gave a hoot and nosed into the traffic. Marie-Claude leant out of the window and waved.

"Bye!' I shouted. Another flourish, and she was gone, this time for good. I turned away sadly, but as I walked back towards the other bus stop that sadness evaporated, to be replaced by inspiration. She had such enthusiam – for travel, for China, for life itself.

'*Ni hao*,' I said to the man in front of me in the queue. He turned and gawped in silent astonishment. A 5 turned up, steam-pressing its passengers. World War III broke out.

The next two buses didn't even bother stopping; the third pulled in but only initiated more violence. I stood back and let the experts fight it out. I didn't want anything to break into this euphoria of mine; I wanted to be whisked straight to Shamian Island, so that I could fill my journal with my new-found spirit, and parcel bits of it into letters home. An idea struck me; I started waving at passing taxis. They're not supposed to stop in the street for business, but one soon did.

'Shamian Island?'

'Okay.'

I jumped in. A slash through the Gordian knot of Guangzhou's transport system: Marie-Claude would have been proud of me.

'*Ni hao*,' I began. The driver slammed shut the glass partition between us and yanked the wheel round in a U-turn.

'Shamian!' I repeated.

'This is quick way,' he replied.

'Ah.' I let myself sink into the seat. Don't get paranoid. The quick way. In comfort, too.

It was only when the meter reached double figures that I began to worry again. Six yuan, our shared taxi to the CAAC office had been; now this one was costing twice that. Click. Twelve yuan twenty, the price of a good meal. ('Treat yourself from time to time,' Marie-Claude had said.) Click. Twelve forty. I was a budget traveller, I shouldn't have been so lazy. Click. Half a day's allowance! I tore my gaze away from the dancing numbers to the street. That building looked familiar. Yes, we passed it five minutes ago.

'Excuse me. Er, I think . . . Hey!'

'Quick way,' said the driver, and turned his cassette to full volume.

As at the border, my Mandarin vanished in an instant. I should tell him about the twice-passed building; I should tell him to stop – now. And refuse to pay. But I did nothing.

'Thir'y two yuan,' were the driver's only other words, as he put me down outside the hotel.

'But that's far too much!'

'Me'er say thir'y two yuan. Please pay with Foreign Exchange Certificate.'

'Guangzhou Youth Hostel, Guangzhou, People's Republic of China. 8 April 1985 . . .' The words refused to flow. My thoughts kept returning to that taximeter, to that music, to my own feeling of helplessness.

Marie-Claude would have known how to deal with him, I told myself.

Marie-Claude's airborne by now, another part of me replied. You're on your own.

Oh, well. It was only a few pounds.

It's not the amount. It's the fact of having been ripped off. The humiliation. The loss of trust – who else is out to get you?

My room, which had been so temperate and airy yesterday evening, had become hot and oppressive. I had to get out and walk – along the riverbank (how ugly it suddenly looked: a sewer full of polystyrene, driftwood, condoms and dead fish) to the mainland, where vehicles thundered like monsters along the bund.

Don't be so silly, I said to myself. This is travel. Adventure.

A man came up with a tray of digital watches. 'Hello!' he chirped. 'You buy?'

'No,' I snapped, then turned on my heels and ran.

'Going somewhere?' said David, a tall thin Londoner who had taken the bed by the window.

'Oh, just a little treat.' I splashed on a bit more aftershave. 'An open-air restaurant I noticed this afternoon. Marie-Claude's advice: the best tonic when you're feeling down.'

He scowled. 'Is she coming with you?'

'No,' I said sadly.

'Ah! Mind if I join you?'

I hesitated.

'I want to celebrate,' he added. 'I'm happy.'

'Oh, well, why not? What's the occasion?'

'I'm leaving.'

A waiter took us to a table right next to a bank of wire cages – death row for a selection of listless, ugly reptiles.

'You like – you eat,' he said.

I shook my head. 'I think I'll try something vegetarian.'

'Wise,' David commented. 'I don't eat meat in China.'

'No? Still, at least you know it's fresh.'

'And you know how it's been treated. Look at the size of those cages. That pangolin can't even turn round.'

We asked for another table.

'So, disillusion has set in already?' said my companion as we sat down. 'That's quick. Well done.'

'What d'you mean?'

He shrugged. 'I thought you were lashing out on a meal to cheer yourself up.'

'Just a mood,' I said, turning my attention to the menu. 'What d'you think Chicken Golden Harmony is?'

'A fancy name for an ordinary dish, I imagine. Typical of China. The Middle Kingdom – land of Oriental mystery. One of the world's nastiest political regimes, with some of its most corrupt officials, its laziest workers, its most vicious secret police –'

'How about Three Happiness Bean Curd?'

'I've no idea. Try privacy, freedom and prosperity: I think you'll find they're off.'

'Look, I've come here to enjoy myself.'

'Sorry.'

I handed him the menu, hoping it would shut him up. It didn't.

'Is that all you came travelling for?' he asked. 'Enjoyment? You can get that at your local bingo hall.'

'No, of course not. Experience, education . . . I was lying in bed one night and suddenly realized how I'd always wanted to go travelling, but never –'

'I'll educate you, if you want.'

'No you won't. You hate this country.'

'So? Is education just hearing what you want to hear?'

'Tonight, yes.'

But it isn't, of course, and conversation edged inevitably back to the land we had both travelled so far to see.

'It's dead,' David was saying. 'Morally, culturally, economically. But tourists don't find that out – sauntering round the big cities, taking their snapshots and grinning at everyone. Seeing flowers from horseback, the Chinese call it. I've been here six months. I've talked to people properly – about their loveless marriages and their menial jobs; about their fear, their anger, their boredom.

'You can't just blame it on Communism, either. China's always been brutal, conformist, authoritarian, xenophobic. Mao was another Qin Shihuang, another Hongwu: grab power by force, rule by terror. People accept it – they act it out themselves. They're accomplices in their own persecution. They're

collectively mad, in my view. Look at the Cultural Revolution.
Mass self-immolation . . .'

I tried arguing back despite my relative inexperience.

'These are your opinions. Other people see things differently.
Marie-Claude –'

David's expression changed instantly. 'Her!' he exclaimed.
'You didn't take her seriously, did you?'

'Yes, of course.'

He began shaking his head. 'Then you must forgive me for
overrating your intelligence.'

'Now hang on –'

He did the opposite. 'I've lost count of the number of people
like Marie-Claude I've met in Asia,' he began. '"Travellers"! This
continent is overrun with them – India, Thailand, Indonesia,
now China. They've all got one thing in common: they don't
give a damn about the East. Not the real East, the one that real
Eastern people have to live in. All "travellers" want is somewhere
different from the West – somewhere they can sort out a few
of their stupid little hang-ups, then sit around in their batik
T-shirts talking about Hermann Hesse or Zen Buddhism. You
ask Marie-Claude about the real China – the one-child policy,
the Central Investigation Bureau, the Gulags in Qinghai – and
see what she knows.'

'She felt very strongly about the invasion of Tibet,' I count-
ered.

'Oh, yeah? Then what's she doing wandering round China
saying how "spiritual" everything is? They're so arrogant,
"travellers", that's what gets me. They set up a little paradise
somewhere: Yunnan, Ladakh, Phuket – wherever. Then they
call anybody who tries to be objective about it all those
fashionable names: insensitive, narrow-minded, ethnocentric.
Narrow-minded, for God's sake! They're the most narrow-
minded people I've ever bloody met . . .'

He caught my eye – something he had been avoiding during
his monologue – and his voice tailed away.

'You liked her, didn't you?'

'Yes.'

'Well, I'm sorry if I was rude. But I've had it up to here
with travellers' talk. How whole everyone in the East is, how

natural. How much better the quality of life is – in India, where families are dying of hunger on the streets; in China, where there are police informers in every apartment block, where there's imprisonment without trial, public executions, slave labour in camps. If there's one thing that sickens me more than that kind of barbarism, it's people like Marie-Claude who patronize it.'

I didn't know what to say, so said nothing. The waiter brought our meals – ten times more expensive than lunch, and not nearly as nice – which we sat eating in silence, listening to the Americans at the next table judging various Asian countries by the quality of dope available. When the bill came, David insisted on paying.

'Tomorrow, I shall be free again.'

As we left, he walked over to the cages and struck them, sending those creatures that could move scurrying around in terror.

'Whenever anybody tells you how wonderful the Chinese are,' he said, 'just take a look at the way they treat animals.'

That night was unbearably humid. I dreamt that I was a pangolin in a cage, writhing and wriggling but unable to change position. I screamed for help – in a language that nobody could understand – and the cage turned into a taxi. We passed a road sign (ALIENS THIS WAY) and I knew something awful was waiting at the end of the alley. A public execution. 'You stand accused of listening to propaganda directed against the People's Republic . . .'

I awoke just in time to avoid the firing squad, and spent the rest of the night fumbling with my bedclothes, half dying to get back to sleep, half dreading the prospect. Morning came painfully slowly, bringing light, reason, order and a soft, untroubled doze. Until David's alarm went off.

'First train to Hong Kong!' he said gleefully as he strode out.

I breakfasted with the two most hippie-looking travellers I could find.

'People are very whole here, aren't they?' I began. 'Natural . . .'

'Hmm,' Klaus replied. He was tall and bony, with a wispy beard and penetrating, intelligent eyes. Far too intelligent. Embarrassed at my opening, I moved the conversation on to his travel experiences, and sat back to listen. I soon found out that I was with another philosopher of the road, though of a different kind from Marie-Claude – Klaus was more in search of limits than answers. When he talked about religion, it was about the strangest, most testing ones: B'on, Tantrism, shamanism. He had tried every drug available in India. He had been trekking illegally in Gilgit and Tibet (losing one of his toes through frostbite). I wanted to be impressed, but the memory of Marie-Claude wouldn't let me. Not because I disbelieved his stories, but because his quest seemed pointlessly introverted: he remained a distant, scary figure, despite his friendliness, while her pilgrimage had made her bloom with generosity and warmth.

'Guangzhou is very westernized,' he was saying. 'This is not a travellers' place. All these fancy things . . .' He pointed at the dog-eared posters of Beijing on the bar walls. 'I leave as soon as possible for Xishuangbanna. We try crossing into Burma. You wish to come?'

'That's kind,' I replied. 'But I have a route planned.'

'Where do you go?'

'Hangzhou, Suzhou, Nanjing . . .' I began tracing out a map on the table, but Klaus was unable to hide his disdain.

'Eastern cities,' he muttered.

'Han China,' I riposted. 'The real East, the one Eastern people have to live in.'

It was the one thing I hadn't wanted to say.

Steffi, his companion, had never looked like uttering a word, and we ate the rest of our meal in silence. When they got up to go, I felt too foolish to say goodbye.

'So,' said Klaus, breaking out into his craggy smile again. 'Today we visit Qingping market. You wish to come?'

It was turning into a blistering day. My sandals felt gummed to the pavement: were they melting on contact with the flagstones, or was it just too much effort to pick my feet up?

'In Turfan, it will be over forty-five degrees Celsius,' said Klaus. 'That will be an experience!'

The market, in a covered alley north of the island, was an experience, too. It was as hot as hell in its crammed aisles, among the jostling, sweating customers, between head-high banks of animal cages. The stink of sweat, mange, offal and excrement was abominable. We squeezed past bowls eddying with slime-green snakes, to the poultry section where chickens and ducks pressed against their coop wire, sticking out gaping, gasping beaks in a vain plea for air and water.

Just look at the way they treat animals, I said to myself.

A rooster gave a cry of terror as it was heaved out for inspection.

'No meat,' said the potential buyer, pinching his fingernails into the breast.

'Plenty,' the vendor replied, nearly yanking off a wing. He dangled it upside down and squeezed a thigh. 'Look!'

A handful of grubby notes changed hands. The new owner tied the bird to his wrist – it fell silent once it was dangling downwards – and barged off into the melee.

Klaus shrugged. 'In country districts they slit the chickens' throats in front of you. When I was in Dali . . .'

Owls on shit-stained perches peered round at this animal mayhem, reacting with a simple, puzzled blink. Conventional wisdom would have them accepting their condition philosophically, but to me they seemed intensely stupid. Didn't they realize what they were here for? The domestic creatures in the next section certainly did: the skeletal, miaowing cats; the whimpering puppies with big, glazed eyes. At least they were offering some kind of protest.

'Those are for eating?' I asked an old lady.

'Of course.' She grinned. 'You want one?'

'No, I –' I turned away, to find myself facing a man with a monkey in a cage.

'You want?'

It had been stuffed in like an object. For a moment I thought it was dead, but the hands that hung out through the bars made a feeble gesture of supplication.

'The monkey brain is the greatest delicacy,' said Klaus. 'At banquets, they slice off the top of the skull . . .'

Before the creatures on offer could get any closer to *Homo sapiens*, the alley debouched into a square. Here, at least, everything was dead. Fish, their eyes haloed by flies. Goats and rabbits – or rather bits of them – strewn across chopping blocks. The chortling sound by my feet, like a stream on an open moor, turned out to be blood flowing down a drain.

'Very clean, Guangzhou,' Klaus began. 'When I was in Kashi –'

'I'm going to be sick,' I said.

I crossed to the mainland and wandered along the embankment, unmoved by the vigour of its pavement markets or the river's idiosyncratic fusion of squalor and beauty. When I reached the footbridge over People's Road, I climbed shakily to the top and stood watching Guangzhou thundering past below. There was nothing left inside me: no feelings, no memories, no expectations, no desires . . .

'*Parlez-vous français?*'

An elderly Chinese man was at my shoulder, smiling and holding out a hand.

'Yes,' I replied. 'I mean *oui. Un peu.*'

'You are English?'

I nodded.

'Where are you going?' he asked.

'Nowhere.'

'Nowhere?'

'Into the town.'

'May I join you?'

We walked along the riverside, Mr Zhu (as he introduced himself) making the pace despite his age and his thick woollen suit.

'I am teacher of languages,' he said. 'Now retired. Now have many young friends from Europe. *Sprechen Sie Deutsch?*'

'*Nein* – not really.'

'*Italiano?*'

'No.'

He shook his head. 'English friends no good at languages. You like tea?'

'Yes, very much.' Especially if we could drink it in the shade.

'Good. We go to Cultural Park.'

Five minutes took us to a fairground with slides, round-abouts and helter-skelters – all shut. At the far end of this ghost paradise was a windowless white building with a glass dome.

'The Grand Ballroom!' Zhu exclaimed. 'We go in?'

'Sure.'

'Some evenings, they have Western dancing here,' he said eagerly as we entered its carpeted foyer. 'Many young people come. Many, many . . .' He smiled at the idea – a disinterested, generous happiness.

Today we were the only customers. The two waitresses gossiping by the cash desk watched in silence as we crossed to a table, then resumed their conversation, their harsh, brittle voices swirling up into the dome to mingle with the Grand Ballroom's other sounds: tinkly Chinese muzak, a plastic fish tank gurgling to itself in a corner, someone washing crockery beyond a half-open door.

'So, how long have you been in China?' Zhu began.

We talked about my travel plans, about Chinese history, about Western politics and literature (why had I been expecting everyone in China to be parochial and ignorant?). I tried to steer conversation round to his life and times, and he smiled.

'My life has been dull.'

'Not to me,' I replied. 'Tell me about China in the early 1950s. What were things like?'

'It was so long ago!' He paused, as if uncertain whether to say any more, then went on. 'But things were good. It was a new start for everybody, even non-Communists. The Japanese were gone; the warlords were gone. People worked hard. The country began to see real prosperity for the first time in its history.'

A waitress brought a pot of tea and a plate of soap-flavoured, boiled sweets; the drink revived my spirits – and, with them, a nagging curiosity. Zhu was reminiscing freely, now, about the Fifties. My thoughts leapt ahead to my own childhood, to the Sixties, to Red China and the terrible Cultural Revolution. Or had it been so terrible? The snippets that I had heard had made it look that way, but were these a biased sample – the news that people expected, the news our media barons wanted us to hear?

'Huaxian I was living in at the time,' Zhu was saying. 'They built a huge factory there . . .'

My curiosity swelled to hunger: I had to hear the truth. And who better to ask than this talkative old man, with his 'many young friends from Europe', with his joy at modern dancing?

'And the Sixties?' I asked, when he came to a halt. 'What really happened in the Cultural Revolution?'

I got my answer instantly. Zhu's sharp, interested eyes flooded with disappointment, and his grin sagged as if it had been held open by two wires which I had just slashed. I made a desperate bid to save the situation – 'And now there's reform!' – but he simply began shaking his head.

'Reform,' he said flatly, after a pause so long that I wondered if I hadn't struck him dumb. 'We had reforms before . . .' He gave an immense shrug of complete, broken resignation. 'It has always been the way in China – after the good times, the bad times come again.'

Then there was silence – except for the fish tank, the muzak and the gossiping waitresses. I glanced up at the roof, down at the dance floor, round at the plastic flowers on the tables – anywhere to avoid Zhu's pathetic expression. After several appalling minutes, he coughed and tapped his watch.

'I must go,' he said. 'Maybe we meet again.'

I watched the old teacher shuffle out through the door. Guilt burst over me – together with an awful relief that I was no longer confronted with his physical presence.

I waited until there was no conceivable chance of catching him up, then paid and left. The bund outside was crowded with Chinese, many in their thirties and forties. By the law of averages, some of them must have been Red Guards. This man, with his executive's briefcase? This woman, in her patterned emerald blouse and clashing, bottle-green slacks? If so, did they now feel any guilt – or just what the Party told them to feel: 'regret' for 'mistakes'? And what would their emotions be tomorrow, if a new set of orders came through?

A man jangled by on a bike, with a chicken swinging from the handlebars. I cursed this country and its cruel, deceitful inhabitants; I hated them, almost as much as I hated myself.

3

Hard Sleeper to Hangzhou

Train 108 wasn't so much a way of getting from one place to another, as a place in itself: a city on wheels. An ancient, mythical city that towered over the platform, gleaming in the sharp, early-morning sunlight. Its citizens swarmed up and down its boarding ladders, stuffing it to its high, domed roof with bulging carrier bags and unshuttable suitcases – the city was preparing itself for a siege. With its formidable and totally modern guardians (People's Liberation Army men at both ends, cradling sub-machine-guns), it would surely be impregnable.

Among the crowds swirling at its feet, I noticed another foreigner. Despite all my resolutions to mix with Chinese only, I found myself following him – but was stopped at his carriage door by a woman in a black serge uniform.

'Ticket?' she snapped. Her silver buttons, embossed with the rising sun and cross-section rail of Chinese Railways, glinted officiously. I uncrumpled the sheet of paper for which I had queued much of yesterday afternoon, and she shook her head.

'This is soft class,' she said. 'You're hard sleeper.'

It suddenly sounded appallingly spartan. There are three classes of travel on Chinese trains: hard seat, hard sleeper and soft sleeper. Klaus, of course, always travelled the first of these, and David the last (calling any other style of travelling 'self-indulgence in artificial discomfort'). Hard sleeper had been Marie-Claude's suggestion. Until a few seconds ago, it had seemed the obvious choice.

As I walked up the platform, I told myself that I would have plenty of time to decide who was the wisest. This train ride took thirty-six hours – across Guangdong to the Nanling Mountains, into the Yangzi basin, across more mountains (the Wuyi Shan) to the Qiantang River, which took us to the old Song-dynasty capital of Hangzhou. A journey of a thousand miles – just a corner cut off this enormous country.

The hard-sleeper attendant had dull brass buttons. But she looked at my ticket with as much disdain as her silver superior before crossing my name off on a clipboard and pointing to the door. I scrambled on board, through a vestibule that stank of disinfectant, into a long corridor with jump seats along one side and open-ended compartments on the other. Each compartment had six bunks, generously padded. Ceiling fans were buzzing round, and when I found my place and sat down by the window, my feet touched a Chinese Railways thermos, ready with boiling water. There was even piped music. Who could ask for more?

The other places filled up as departure-time approached. A middle-aged man in a Western suit took the one next to me.

'*Ni hao,*' I said.

He didn't reply.

A fat youth in a Mao jacket sat opposite him.

'*Ni hao,*' I said.

He didn't reply, either.

A young woman in red slacks and a pink jumper occupied the other window seat.

'*Ni hao,*' I said. She at least smiled, then turned to gaze sadly out on the platform. At what – or whom? But I'd have to guess: only the carriage tannoy seemed to want to communicate, reminding us not to leave luggage on the platform, then launching into the third melancholy, twanging folk tune in a row.

We left dead on time, picking up speed through the shanty towns and building sites of the suburbs and rattling out into the country, where the beauty of the rice fields filled me once more with joy. Their winding black banks; their inexhaustible variety of shape, colour and texture; their slow, purposeful cultivators – had I forgotten so quickly? Then we gave up our momentum to pull into a tiny station, where two passengers got on. We waited for an oncoming train, because the main line out of Guangzhou was only one-track.

And we waited. Frustration began building up inside me – thirty-six hours of stops and starts? – then vanished instantly as a steam engine came into view. Good God, I hadn't seen such a thing since childhood! It was even larger than I remembered steam locos to be – at least seventy feet from the front of its barrel-chested boiler to the end of the rectangular long-haul coal tender. And it shook and snorted in a way I had almost (but not quite) forgotten, like a live creature – a dragon in harness but still only half tamed.

Before it could get into a fight with our diesels, the engine branched off into a goods siding, where minions began placating it with water from an overhead tank. Its master wiped his forehead and climbed down out of his cab. He had a right to be proud. China is the only country in the world still manufacturing these monsters – a fact usually quoted as an example of its backwardness, of its lingering Stalinist love affair with inefficient, outmoded heavy industries. But these pistons, connecting rods and huge, scarlet drive wheels made it more than just an object: it was art, a sculpture on the theme of work, determination and energy; a celebration of a new nation stretching out and discovering its strength.

Our diesels gave a soft, envious moo on their klaxons, and dragged us off into a more romantic China.

There had to be some way of getting a conversation going.

'Smoke?' I said, holding out a packet of duty-free. The lady opposite shook her head with an air of disapproval; the fat youth took one but said nothing. Nobody else responded. I lit up so as not to look stupid, and resumed my gazing out of the window. I didn't even like cigarettes. A series of numbered telegraph poles began: Chinese numerals – good reading practice.

'*Ling ling yi. Ling ling er . . .*' I wondered how many it would take to get to Hangzhou. *Shi wan*, a hundred thousand? And all without a word being spoken? '*Ling ling qi. Ling ling ba . . .*' Well, it served me right. From the teeming streets of Guangzhou, only one lonely old man had wanted my company – and look how I had repaid him.

'*Qing wen . . .*'

Someone was tapping my shoulder: the man in the suit. He was talking to me. I turned and listened – and couldn't understand a word. He stopped, perhaps wondering whether it was worth carrying on, then repeated very slowly: '*Ni shi Mei-guo ren* [are you American]?'

'*Bushi*,' I replied. '*Yingguo ren.*'

'Ah, you are English!'

'Yes!' I exclaimed, doubly happy that he spoke my language. The man introduced himself as Dr Ye. 'You are married?' he added.

'No.'

'Brother and sister?'

'No.'

His brow furrowed. 'Your parents – still alive?'

'Yes.'

'Ah.' He nodded sympathetically: without a family, one is nobody. 'And your profession?'

'Music,' I said. 'Publishing, that is.'

'Ah.' Ye pointed at the loudspeaker. 'You like our music? This is folk tune.'

'Folk,' I replied, correcting his pronunciation: he had said 'fuck', which I found funny for an instant, then embarrassing.

'Folk, folk . . . How much do you earn?'

'About eight hundred yuan.'

'A year?'

'No – er, a month.' Ye's eyes rounded in amazement. I had lied (eight hundred yuan was a hundred and sixty pounds, about what I earned in a week), but not outrageously enough.

'You must be rich man!'

'No. You see, everything is expensive in England. For example, my room costs a hundred and fifty yuan a week.'

'A hundred and fifty yuan!' He grinned. 'You have room in Buckingham Palace, I think.'

Pole twenty-four rattled by. Marriage, family, profession, income – and I had half imagined we would talk about tractors or pig iron.

'We see Mrs Thatcher on television,' said Ye, after a pause. 'She is strong ruler, I think.'

'Yes.' Time to open things out. 'Like Deng Xiaoping?'

34

My companion looked shocked, then took a magazine from his briefcase. 'This is American article on computers,' he said. 'Please – you help me with some of the terms.'

Midday. The fat youth had filled a mess tin from the thermos and was making himself a lunch of instant noodles. Someone else produced a length of sugar cane out of a plastic bag and began to gnaw. The sounds of crunching and swallowing; the smells of spices and pasta.

'Where can I get something to eat?' I asked.

'I don't know,' Ye replied. I hadn't been much help with his computer terms, and he seemed to have lost interest in our conversation. Maybe I'd got a tone wrong and said something unspeakably rude instead of explaining what 'flip-flop' meant.

A few minutes later he stood up and vanished down the corridor. I suddenly felt very lonely: pole eight hundred and sixty-three went by, and each one took me further and further into this incomprehensible country.

'Please.' The doctor was back, holding out a polystyrene box of rice, cabbage and goose wing. 'For you.'

I reached for my wallet.

He shook his head vehemently. 'You are a guest,' he added.

The whole compartment watched me eat. When I had finished, they offered me biscuits, sugar cane, tea. The food was coarse and tasteless, but the kindness of the donors made this as pleasurable a meal as I had ever eaten. The harshness of Guangzhou was just a memory: travelling, I realized, meant motion, and motion meant change, a perpetual chance to start again.

As I drank the last of my tea, the woman opposite lowered her paperback romance and spoke.

'*Ni shi Meiguo ren?*'

She knew no English, so we invented our own language out of Mandarin, mime and scribbles on the flap of my guidebook. Her name was Yang; she came from Yichun; she was a student at the academy of traditional Chinese medicine in Guangzhou; she specialized in acupuncture.

'Traditional medicine is more familiar to ordinary people,' she explained. 'And it's cheaper; cures can cost a few fen. Western medicine is good for the cities; in the countryside, the old ways are still the most effective.'

Dr Ye scowled at this point. 'Scientific theories are either true or false,' he put in.

Yang ignored him. 'And what about your profession?' she asked.

'Music –' I began.

Before I could finish, her cheap, overapplied lipstick cracked into a broad smile. 'Music?' she exclaimed. 'That's wonderful!' Her eyes started to shine with pleasure. 'I love music! Listen!' She started to 'la' a tune, in a clear, soulful voice.

'That's "Auld Lang Syne"!'

She nodded. 'All Chinese love music. We learn songs from all over the world. Listen!'

'Good God – "Jingle Bells"!'

Her sad, musicianlike manner gave the latter song an air of untapped depth. Just as well she didn't know the lyrics. She didn't know the middle eight bars, either, so I sang them for her; then we ran through them together: a glorious, absurd moment of communion, of sharing that instant delight that music-making can bring. Then she shot a glance at the other travellers and fell silent.

'Up to C,' I said.

She shook her head and turned the colour of her slacks. I peered round the compartment: eyes were upon us – not hostile or even disapproving, but watching.

Damn you all, I thought, then remembered their recent kindness.

'You sing very beautifully,' I said.

Yang couldn't restrain a smile before wriggling back into the safety of her novel.

The landscape had been flat since Guangzhou, but now a line of hills was advancing towards us. Our pace dropped; the note of the engines rose. We had reached Nanling Shan. The train began snaking up a valley, vanishing into short, clattering tunnels then leaping out on to iron trestle bridges. The sedate river beside us fell away and began to froth and swirl; scrub and fir trees replaced the bamboo and palms that had lined the trackside.

Signs of human habitation vanished altogether, except for a few foresters' huts and, at the top of a pass, a small town that clung to the railway as if nothing else could prevent it sliding into what was now a deep gorge beneath us.

'Train wait fifteen minutes,' said Ye, as the engines ground gratefully to a stop at the wooden wild-west station. The man with the sugar cane suggested getting out for a walk.

On the platform, it was more like Scotland in autumn than spring a couple of degrees north of the tropics. Rock cliffs towered over our heads and vanished into the low, grey mist that had swallowed the sun miles back. Below, damp brick houses with rain-bright tin roofs wound down towards the river, whose boom echoed around the gorge walls like the sound of an advancing but as yet unseen army. I shuddered – with cold, I thought at first; then, I realized, with excitement.

I'm in China. Me! On a mountain halt in Hunan province.

The thought sent a thrill fizzing through me, as passionate and irrational as those unexpected moments of adolescent self-awareness – the ones that tell you that life is infinitely more rewarding than had seemed possible a second ago.

Me . . .

I had forgotten myself capable of moments like that. They had stopped as causelessly as they had started, in early adulthood – and I hadn't regretted their passing: confusion and fear always followed in their wake. But now, whatever had seized my spirits and swept them skyward just let me float gently back down to earth – that is, to a rickety wooden platform several hundred feet above a furious torrent of water.

Yang had retired to her upper bunk and was finishing her romance, comfortlessly squeezed between pieces of the fat youth's luggage. My friend from the platform, Mr Ren, took her seat and appointed himself my guide.

'Jinggang Shan,' he said, pointing left. 'The cradle of our revolution!' He beamed at me proudly, as if he had been there himself with Mao and Zhu De. And that way's Ruijing, where the Long March began. The Sixth Army crossed the Beijiang river near here.' This time he pointed to our right, at that angry, unforgiving water.

I shivered again. The Communists had already been close to starvation when their march began. Five thousand miles of the worst terrain in the world lay ahead of them: numerous rivers like this one, mountain passes up to sixteen thousand feet, lifeless swamps hundreds of miles across – and all the time they were under harassment from an enemy with a bigger army and monopoly of the air. Out of every ten partisans who had set off, only one had reached Yan'an. It was a story of heroism unparalleled in Western history: I could only marvel at it. What fortitude, idealism and discipline! I felt pampered and aimless on my padded seat, with my tea thermos the stretch of an arm away. But then – quite uninvited – another picture came into my mind: an old man's eyes fixing me across a table in Guangzhou's Grand Ballroom, brimful of disappointment and heartbreak. In the long term, what had all the valour and sacrifice achieved?

It was still early when the rest of the passengers turned in. I lay on my berth with my notebook, trying to recall the Mandarin words I had learnt during the day. *Zhenci* – acupuncture. *Zhenci* –

'Lights out soon,' Ye interrupted, pointing at his watch. A few minutes later, the loudspeaker bade us goodnight and the compartment went dark, leaving only the dim, blue glow of the frosted bulbs along the corridor. I lay listening to the shuffling of my fellow travellers and the relentless tattoo of the wheels. Beyond them the Beijiang river crashed through the darkness towards the China Sea. So much idealism, so much waste – this country's life might have been my own.

'Good morning!' the speaker chirped. 'We are in Jiangxi province.' It was five thirty. I rolled over and looked blearily round at the other passengers. All my friends from yesterday had vanished into one or other of the sodium-lit echo chambers where we had stopped during the night. What would they be doing now? (Sleeping, if they had any sense.) In a week's time? In a year?

'Anyone speak English?' I asked.

Nobody answered. When I offered round the cigarettes, I got smiles and thanks in a dialect that I couldn't understand. It was going to be a long day.

Overnight, Train 108 had become a local service, stopping at the tiniest stations, always to take on more passengers than got off. Soon five or six people were squeezed on to each row of seats, and the corridor had filled up with bags, bikes, buckets and baskets. A trip to the lavatory meant barging past staring, grumbling peasants; tripping over luggage; waiting in a queue. Back in my compartment, the fan lost power and flapped round aimlessly with the motion of the carriage. The air became stale and damp, and my head began to spin. Tea, that was what I wanted. But the thermos was empty, and the samovar was at the far end of the corridor, in the attendant's cabin. I should concentrate on something, read about the Long March – Edgar Snow's *Red Star Over China*. But the man next to me kept jabbing his elbow into my ribs. And somebody's suitcase had taken up my leg room. And the fellow opposite was chain-smoking cheap, acrid Flying Horse cigarettes. Even the window had lost its magic: Jiangxi province was a place of rocks and rain, of grey-walled communes, flooded roads and groups of drenched matchstick figures hacking miserably at the earth.

I began to feel hungry. Dr Ye had advised me to eat 'soft class': I had told myself I wouldn't, that I'd travel the way other 'hard' travellers did. Besides, how could I sit wolfing soft-class food while out there people scraped for subsistence (and their forebears had died for lack of it)? But when lunchtime came, these objections suddenly seemed fatuous. Imagine trying to explain my unforced abstinence to a Jiangxi peasant . . . At the next station, I got off and walked down along the empty, weed-covered platform. Nobody challenged me as I climbed on board the dining car. Its carpeted floor, tasseled curtains and white linen tablecloths smiled as I entered – they had been expecting me.

The foreigner that I had seen at Guangzhou sat alone at one of the tables. I walked up and asked if I could join him.

'Okay,' he said.

I sat down. He didn't speak. I felt obliged to.

'So, how long have you been here?'

'About half an hour.'

'No, I mean, in China.'

'Eight months. Why?'

'Oh, just curiosity. Enjoying it?'

'Of course not.'

He went back to staring out at the scenery; there wasn't much alternative to following his example. We passed a huge brown mesa, its sides gouged out by frothing streams; we stopped in a tin-roofed city of factories, chimneys, mud roads and huts, all glimmering with rain; we rolled on to a bridge of black iron girders. Half way across, the man turned to me and spoke.

'You've just arrived, haven't you?'

After which, he couldn't stop. All the indignities he, Georg, had suffered as a student in Shanghai came pouring out of him: endless rote learning; cramped, unhealthy accommodation; inadequate food . . .

'And they don't let us mix with the Chinese at all. It's apartheid. They put us in a separate dormitory block and keep a note of whoever comes to visit. Our warden hates foreigners. She was a Red Guard, and still calls anyone who "fraternizes" with us a "traitor". One of our lecturers made friends with a group of students from London. She used to come and practise her English; she showed them round Shanghai; they invited her to their parties. One day she started making excuses to avoid meeting up. Then her lectures were cancelled. We couldn't contact her. Later, we found out she'd been accused of spying, denounced in front of her colleagues, and dismissed.'

He fiddled edgily with the silver-plated cruet as he spoke, as if he suspected that there was a bug in the salt.

'D'you speak Mandarin?' he asked, lowering his voice.

'A little.'

'Wait till you understand what they say behind your back. *Lao maozi* – hairy ones. *Yang guizi* – foreign devils. Barbarians. Dogs. Ghosts. They hate us,' he added, his voice dropping still further, to a whisper. 'That's the truth. Always have, always will.'

'*Zhongfan?*' the waiter shouted at Georg's shoulder, slapping a torn plastic menu on the table. My companion nearly jumped out of his skin.

We ate in silence, scrutinized by the staff: two young, giggling waitresses; two men in chef's hats; the maître d' with his stained white coat. They outnumbered their customers easily. To follow the main course, I ordered coffee; tea arrived instead, which I drank slowly to delay my return to my compartment. Finally Georg's gloom became too much. I paid and began barging my way back, dreaming that Yang, Ren and Ye would be there to greet me. Instead, someone had taken my seat.

'You shouldn't be here,' I said, flapping my reservation in front of him. But I didn't understand the ticket and he didn't understand my Mandarin. I ended up squeezing between him and the man with the elbows. Both of them grinned and shunted along as I tried to wriggle myself a little extra space, but mistrust had been sown in my mind. Barbarians, dogs, ghosts – what were they really thinking?

In mid-afternoon, two middle-aged men in grey flannel jackets boarded. When they had evicted the people opposite me with a simple wave of their travel passes and made themselves infuriatingly comfortable, one of them took a piece of folded cardboard from his pocket and opened it into a square. The other produced a box of draughts pieces with characters on, which he lined up on the board in opposing rows – black versus red. *Xiangqi*, Chinese chess.

The game began slowly, the front line shuffling forward like pawns, a kind of knight zigzagging from the back into the centre of the board. Two pieces stood unmoved in a special middle row. Just as I thought I understood the rules, black spring-heeled one of them directly over an occupied square. In reply to this aggression, the red 'castle' took off. '*Jiang!*', I soon discovered, meant 'Check'. Two moves later I learnt that '*Jiangsi!*' meant 'Checkmate'. *Jiangsi* in Jiangxi . . .

The winner set up a second contest, but his colleague looked up at me.

'Do you want a game?' he asked in Mandarin.

'I'd love one,' I replied, astounded. 'But, well, I don't know the rules.'

He nodded thoughtfully, then pointed to the 'knight'. 'This is the horse,' he began.

News that a Westerner was planning to challenge a Chinese at *xiangqi* spread fast, and a crowd of leathery, crew-cut spectators came pressing into our compartment. I gazed back at them, wondering what was going on in their minds. *Yang guizi?* All I could see was stares and smiles.

'You start.'

I hesitated.

'Try this.'

Canon (*Pao*, the jumping piece) to centre three: my first move in *xiangqi*.

I lost, of course. Several times in rapid succession, despite the patience of my teachers. So I let them return to their contest and went back to my window, triumphant in defeat. My head now buzzed with pieces and moves; with canons, bishops and knights; with the mistakes I had made and the gambits that had tricked me. This was more than a marvellous game – this was a handhold on China, a way to make friends, to enter Chinese life, to stop being an immiscible globule of oil in the great sea flowing all round me. I would make everything, everything, everything I could of it.

'We are now in Zhejiang province,' the speaker quacked. Though the landscape was greener and gentler than in Jiangxi, the rain ensured that it was no more cheerful: clouds scraped along the hilltops, curtaining them in grey; bicycles floundered along the trackways, through moonscape puddles cratered with ripples; huddles of peasants stood at level crossings, watching enviously from under home-made kagoules of sacking or tarpaulin. Along the trackside, next to the stone-topped, conical burial mounds (long banned by the authorities but still lovingly maintained), the official lines of saplings threw themselves around in the wind like madmen. Beneath us, the swollen brown rivers roared insults as we rumbled across them. Darkness began to fall. Soon I would have to leave the wheeled city for one that was cold, landbound and unfamiliar.

I was not to be allowed the luxury of self-pity. At a small country station, a stocky, mustachioed man got on.

'*Hao a* [hi]!' he said, shaking the rain off his Mao jacket and squeezing in beside me. I offered him a cigarette; in return he told me a story full of animal impressions, which doubled up the passenger on the other side of me with laughter. For a moment I felt the pain of the child made 'pig in the middle', but then the absurdity of the situation overcame me: Zhejiang dialect blasting into one of my ears; helpless, high-pitched giggles into the other. I started laughing, too, which set the storyteller off on a new round of animal noises – this time with the creature's name added for my benefit.

'Mooo! *Niu.*'

'*Niu.*'

The man corrected my pronunciation (second tone – rising – the most difficult one).

'*Niu!*' That was better. Now I should reply in kind. 'Woof! Woof! Dog.' (I looked to see if there were any snide looks, the way there would be had Georg's hypothesis been true. There weren't.)

'Do'.'

'No, do-g.'

'Do-g. Do-g.'

Soon the whole compartment sounded like a playground, ringing with laughter and animal noises. Only the chess players remained aloof from the frivolity, glancing at me with the disappointed look of teachers who have caught a star pupil smoking with the school toughs. Maybe they were right: as well as learning, I seemed to be regressing on this train journey – to adolescence in the mountains, now into jolly infantilism.

'Quack, quack – duck. Du-ck.'

'Du-ck.'

Who cared? This was fun!

The rhythm of the wheels started to falter. Lights were shining through the rain-streaked window. Streets, factories – we were entering somewhere big.

'Hangzhou?' I asked. Most of the day I had been longing for the moment of arrival; now I wanted never to stop. The storyteller nodded, and I hauled my rucksack unwillingly down from the rack, adult and alone again.

'Remember to take all your belongings,' the loudspeakers nagged. Train 108 – which was going on to Shanghai – squealed to a halt.

'*Zaijian,*' I said. Hands went up for me to shake. My immediate neighbours. The chess players. The other people in the compartment. A couple of guys in the corridor.

'*Zaijian.*'
'*Zaijian.*'
'*Zaijian.*'

A last smile, and I squeezed down the corridor and climbed out into the rain.

The taxi drove down bare, gloomy streets towards Huanhu Lu, where the guidebook assured me I would find accommodation.

'Xihu [West Lake]!' the driver exclaimed, as we turned a corner and emerged on the esplanade of Hangzhou's famous beauty spot. He put me down opposite a hotel. As I got out, my ears filled with sea sounds (boats creaking against moorings, waves sucking at breakwaters) and I hurried instead to the water's edge for my first view.

Beauty? A string of coloured bulbs, about half of which worked, swayed violently in the wind, vanishing north and south into the storm. Beneath me, the West Lake threw itself against the concrete embankment with a frightening, repetitive fury; a few yards out from the wall, the white wave crests disappeared into oceanic blackness.

'*Meiyou,*' said the receptionist at the hotel. No room. Try next door.

I did.

'*Meiyou.*'

A third '*Meiyou*', and the front seemed to run out of hotels. By now rain was streaming down my back and my feet were soaked.

But I was happy: I had made friends in the city on wheels.

4

Tao and the Art of Travelling

The rain kept falling.

Not just while I was splashing along the esplanade to the last possible hotel; not just for my first full day in Hangzhou, when I went out shopping for English winter clothes and came back with Asian flu. It rained for the whole time I was in the old Song-dynasty capital. The weather made Hangzhou the fulfilment of every gloomy prophecy I had heard in the West: it was drab, unfriendly, uniform – a city of Mao suits and work boots, of lowered, suspicious eyes and tightly shut mouths; a study in umbrella black, cloud grey, mud brown and boiler-suit blue.

Except for the Xihu Café. Its owner, a local entrepreneur with wealthy cousins in Singapore, had set it up to attract Westerners, painting the inside bright colours, and kitting it out with tubular steel chairs and an Italian coffee machine (which he spent every spare moment polishing). Instead, his establishment had been adopted by Chinese teenagers of a kind that I hadn't believed existed. Offspring of top Party cadres (according to the owner), they sat round the bar drinking small, expensive cups of espresso coffee, smoking American cigarettes and gambling for ten-yuan notes. The boys wore leather jackets and studded belts, the girls mini skirts and black stockings. Ordinary Hangzhou women had to make do with slacks and pink pop-socks.

At first I was delighted by their rebelliousness, but the longer I looked at these characters, the more ludicrous they appeared.

Their shades and leathers were just as much a uniform as that of the Great Helmsman look-alikes plodding past outside; their style was borrowed from another civilization and another era, from 1950s America – just like Daddy's bulbous, gas-guzzling Hongqi limousine.

'Hi,' I said to the couple next to me, trying to make conversation. They took one look at my new, purple Xihu sweater and my new Xihu galoshes, and turned away with fashionable contempt. I wasn't that upset.

I had set myself a timetable for my journey, though Marie-Claude had assured me I wouldn't keep to it. And sure enough, the date for leaving Hangzhou came and went. Two days later, I still coughed miserably if I went out for more than a few minutes. I had used the last of the Western remedies I'd brought with me (they hadn't been much use, anyway) and, if anything, I was beginning to feel worse again. So I consulted my town plan and fought my way on to a bus, squeezing up next to a man with half his head bandaged in gauze (nobody offered him a seat). When he got off, I did, too – at the Hospital of Chinese Medicine.

Half the other passengers went with us, limping, hobbling and wheezing into the entrance hall, which was already crammed with patients, either queuing at windows or milling around in the centre. None of the windows was marked; a voice called out a series of meaningless numbers over a tannoy; the air was full of pungent herbal smells, none of which I could recognize. A feeling of utter disorientation flooded over me – as in Shenzhen station or that pitch-black temple – and for a second I wanted to run to the door. Then reason reasserted itself. If I waited long enough, some pattern would emerge. In the meantime, I should just join a line.

Five minutes later, a man in white overalls and a round, white, cotton hat walked up to me.

'Hello!' He grinned, maybe to show me what perfect teeth he had. 'You are American?'

'No, er, English.'

'Ah! And you are ill?'

'I have a cough,' I replied, suddenly overcome with shame: all around me were old ladies tottering on sticks, silent children cradled in the arms of anxious parents, and labourers with wounds suppurating through dirty dressings.

'I am Dr Liao Zichen. Please – I make examination.'

I hesitated.

'This way, please.'

I expected to be followed upstairs by a hundred eyes burning with envy – but nobody even noticed.

A tall, mildewy corridor lined with posters of lungs, tar and cigarettes led to the surgery. There were several names on the door, some just in Chinese, others in Chinese and English.

'Our work team,' said the young man proudly.

The room was huge and almost totally empty, apart from a chair and a desk in the centre, a bed in one corner and a table by the window with a mysterious metallic-blue electrical gadget on top. The walls were as bleak, with just one adornment: a chart of the human body, criss-crossed with coloured lines that corresponded to no anatomical system I had ever seen. An alien being, from a world even stranger than China.

'Taoist yin-yang theory of medicine,' said Liao. 'Please – I tell you about it. And you correct my English.' He picked up a pointer

'Chart shows channels by which *qi* flows through human body. *Qi* is vital energy, life force. For health, it must flow freely and naturally, in an orderly manner. Okay so far?'

'Yes,' I replied.

'There are eleven systems in body, five yin and six yang. They store, distribute and harness *qi*. Damage to any one will affect the whole body, producing imbalance and illness. This is the tiger artery . . .'

I wanted to learn, but was soon lost in this bizarre maze – to master a whole new map of the human body in one sitting was beyond anyone's capabilities, surely. My attention began to wander – to my teacher's fishbowl glasses, to that gadget by the window, to the courtyard outside, where two men were wheeling a dead body on a trolley. What happened to your *qi* when you died? I wondered. Indeed, where did death fit into Liao's model of man, where the body was (if I had understood correctly) naturally healthy, where the role of doctors was only to iron out temporary disturbances in its usual benevolent functioning? Nowhere, I realized: Taoist adepts claimed to have the secret of eternal life. But that was absurd.

'Well, that's about it,' the young doctor was saying. 'You follow okay?'

'I got a bit lost in the middle.'

He nodded. 'Now we make examination.'

'Examination?'

'Of your cough.'

He went out, and returned with two colleagues. I had to say 'Aaaah' and stick out my tongue, take off my shirt and get prodded in the back. Then all three went into a huddle to discuss my case. (Was traditional medicine really 'easier to administer'?) A verdict was reached.

'Cupping,' said Liao.

'Ah.' I tried to sound knowledgeable.

The young man opened a drawer and took out two wooden pots. They had small spikes inside them, on which he impaled globules of paste from a jar with a yellowing label. An assistant struck a match and set the paste alight.

'Your *qi* will be attracted by the suction,' said Liao. 'Please lean forward.'

The cups tickled playfully as he placed them on my back. Then, as the smouldering paste fixed the oxygen inside, they began to claw at my skin. 'Take us seriously!' they were saying. I looked up at the chart. *Qi*: life force. Was there such a thing? If so, was it being attracted to two points on my back right now? I tried to feel something – not just an unpleasant pinching but some inner movement, a change of state inside my whole body. Instead, all that came to me was a cynical Western voice.

Take you seriously? Why on earth should we? Here are our veins, our nerves, our synapses. Show us your tiger artery! Measure *qi* for us!

But the Taoist system offered so much: natural well-being, freedom and order coinciding without conflict. My eye roved round the room and fell again on the apparatus by the window. Here, among the herb cups and acupuncture needles, was a product of Western science, with wires, lights, crocodile clips, volt- and ammeters. Could the two traditions communicate, after all?

I pointed to the device and asked what it was.

'Our acupuncture machine,' Liao replied, surprised. My excitement grew.

'What does it do?'

'I'll show you.' The young doctor picked it up and carried it carefully over, plugging it into the main, loading a cassette into a port and twiddling a couple of black Bakelite knobs to rouse its sleeping dials.

'Listen.' Liao handed me a pair of earphones made from an old stethoscope, and I put them on. They were buzzing softly – the machine loading data from the cassette? Then a slow hiss began, ebbing and flowing like waves. Biofeedback? Alpha rhythms? It had such a peaceful quality. Perhaps it was *qi* itself – my own life force, coursing through my tiger artery. A thrill gripped me – the thrill of the unknown.

An instant before it happened, I knew what the sound was – leader tape. Then a string orchestra struck up, in waltz time, and Andy Williams began to croon: 'Moon river . . .'

I waited till the song was over to ask if the machine did anything else, but when the last chord had floated downstream, the question died on my lips. Supposing the answer was no? My faith in *qi*, in yin and yang, maybe even in the Middle Kingdom itself, would be destroyed irrevocably.

'Great,' I said.

'Very romantic song,' said Liao, popping the cups off my back. 'Now, please come to dispensary.'

We went downstairs, to all that waiting and suffering, and jumped the queue again.

Hangzhou's ferry terminal. The clock on the harbourmaster's office was rusted immobile at four thirty-five; everywhere else was in perpetual motion – the churning, oil-black water; the teeming quays; the hulklike iron passenger barges filling and filling with people. Stevedores bobbed up gangplanks with barrels and baskets strapped to their backs; a crowd clamoured angrily behind a barrier while an official argued with one man about a ticket; sailors were heaving on bamboo poles to punt the barge next to us out into the basin. In theory, we would be next – pushed off from our mooring, roped into a train and towed off on to the world's first major inland waterway: Da Yunhe, China's Grand Canal.

'We're three hours late!' I muttered, unmoved by this scene.

My cabinmate shrugged. 'How old did you say this canal was? Fifteen hundred years? What's a few hours? Fancy some *cha*?' he asked me, while miming the question to our neighbours, the Zhangs.

Don was a small, stocky Australian. About thirty, he looked older, with his tweed jacket and the pipe which he kept filled with rough local tobacco (when he couldn't find anything 'more interesting'). Back home, he was a carpenter – for which he had trained by taking a degree in linguistics. The subject had bored him so much that he hadn't even bothered to learn Mandarin for his visit to China. Wood, on the other hand . . .

'Pine,' he said, rapping the table on which the tea urn stood. 'Lousy quality. Look at that knot. Back home, we'd chuck that away.'

His other great interest, it later emerged, was philosophy. But, like Marie-Claude, he kept that in reserve. He had met too many sceptics. We filled our mugs and joined the young Chinese couple, an engineer and his schoolteacher wife.

'How did you enjoy our city?' Mr Zhang asked.

'Er, the weather was bad,' I replied.

'But you saw our beautiful temple of Lingyin Si?' his partner put in. 'The carvings are among the finest in China.'

'I wasn't very well. I had flu.'

'I'm sorry. You went to the temple of General Yue Fei, of course? That is so beautiful.'

'I tried. It's closed for restoration.'

'Oh. General Yue Fei was great Song-dynasty hero.'

Silence fell, apart from Don rasping on his pipe and another squall of rain pattering on the porthole.

'I like this harbour,' I said, suddenly ashamed at my lack of enthusiasm. 'It's got character.'

'It's old!' said Zhang.

When we finally set off, it was past long-abandoned wharves and foul-smelling mudbanks. Even the houses that jutted over the water on rotting wooden stilts turned their backs on the old canal (now an open sewer, plied by rusting hulks). Did modern

China treat all its heritage like this? I had been warned that it did
– serve me right for not listening. Darkness fell early, the lights
of the city gradually thinning out and being replaced by our own
glow bouncing back off the chalk banks. At nine o'clock this
illumination was switched off. Don turned in, already attuned to
Chinese hours; I lay in my bunk, listening to the throb of the tug
and the hiss of the rain, while my thoughts drifted homewards.
Good food, a comfortable bed, health . . . What the hell was I
doing here?

'YMCA!'

The cabin tannoy woke us at five thirty. I wandered out
on deck and stood listening to Village People while Jiangsu
province slid by. The culture clash would have been too much
at any hour.

Zhang joined me. 'Good morning. You slept well?'

'Yes,' I lied.

A man cycling along the towpath spotted me and waved. I
waved back. No sense in self-pity – this was a new day, a new
start. The Grand Canal had fully recovered from its slight at the
hands of Hangzhou and now it was filled with water transport
of all kinds, its life force flowing freely again. Yin or yang? I
wondered. A siren boomed and a posse of tugs came nosing past
with their swaying train of iron-hulled barges, at least twenty of
them, loaded to danger level with sand, coal, wood, piping and
bricks. Yang – it had to be. Then we passed a tall-masted sampan
tacking back and forth under a plain white sail – so delicate, so
yin. Then a tramp ship with a festoon of motor tyres round its
bows – which probably didn't care what it was, as long as it got
its foul-smelling load of dung delivered.

At about eight o'clock, we passed Baodai Qiao, a Tang-
dynasty bridge now disfigured by a line of telegraph poles
across the middle. An hour later we were in Suzhou and
being fêted with noise and activity. This city fronted on to the
waterway: its boatyards sizzled and flashed with blow torches;
its wharves were lined with cranes that nodded and swung their
heads in welcome.

'Hello!' cried a ferryman punting a nest of passengers and bikes
from one bank to the other.

'Hello!' I yelled in reply. Our tug joined in with a whoop on its hooter, happy to be returning home. I knew I was going to like this place.

We docked by a series of tin huts. At the foot of the gangplank, a special reception committee for foreign guests was waiting.

'Hotel?'

'City map?'

'Rickshaw?'

Don pushed through them with a smile and a wave of his Lonely Planet guide. I fell behind deliberately, mindful of Marie-Claude's advice that travellers should make their own discoveries.

'You coming?' the Australian shouted.

I shook my head – then grabbed my pack and headed after him.

A wide, straight boulevard took us into the town centre, down a line of knobbly anglepoise plane trees, past the walls of old mandarins' mansions and the sleepy-looking pavement vendors with their maps, pot plants and souvenirs. This town was bright, spacious and unhurried.

'Lucky old Wang,' said Don.

'Wang?'

'A mate from college. Well, someone I've met. His family live here. He said that if I came to Suzhou, I should look him up.'

'What – go round and visit him?'

I could hardly contain my excitement. I had no contacts of any kind in the People's Republic; I had prepared myself for two months of brief, casual encounters on trains, in cafés, in the streets. If I could enter a Chinese home . . .

'That's if I can find his address,' the Australian continued. 'It's not with the others in my notebook. I'll have a look once we get a room.'

Oh yes. A room . . . We marched up a tarmac drive and were turned away by a uniformed doorman. A new, and already shabby, backpackers' hotel across the road was full. At a third place . . .

'Once you've heard one *Meiyou*, you've heard 'em all,' said Don. 'But there's always somewhere.'

*

Old Suzhou was a city of canals. As we bumped down the *hutongs* on our rented Phoenix bikes, they shadowed us like secret agents, appearing momentarily between two buildings, then vanishing – though we knew they were never far away. Canals had made rebuilding here impossible, ensuring that the old city retained its low, white houses and narrow alleys. They made exploration here a perpetual adventure: a carefully chosen road would suddenly end in a wharf; an apparent dead end would swing round a corner and become a magnificent stone bridge arching out of the jumble of grey-tiled roofs. We'd roll down to a towpath and stop to watch a boatman quietly at work, punting sacks of rice along a backwater to the sound of a radio. We'd stand over a branch of the Grand Canal while steamers and barges chugged past beneath us.

'If you can't get lost somewhere, it's not worth visiting,' said Don, as we asked the way for the umpteenth time.

Our reception was always warm. The people who lived in these back streets (and kept them so clean) were proud, friendly and curious.

'You are Americans? . . . Ah. And where have you been in China?'

Don rattled off a list of places.

'And how do you like Suzhou?'

'The best,' I replied.

None of the directions we received were much use. We ended up, not at the address Don had found on a scrap of paper at the bottom of his rucksack, but down a cul-de-sac at the gates of a factory. A group of workmen, covered in coal dust, watched us skid to a halt.

'*Ni hao*,' I said.

'Hello!' they chanted back, then fell silent, their English vocabulary exhausted.

I paused, thinking what to say next: this was a special moment. At last, I was face to face with the workers of the People's Republic, those iron men of a thousand propaganda posters, in whose name China martialled her military and productive forces (not to mention her forces of political control). They were all grinning with embarrassment.

'Cigarette?' I began.

About fifteen heads nodded in acceptance. In return, the tallest of the men offered me one of his home-rolled. Another took a lighter out of his pocket and held it out ostentatiously. It didn't work. He began tinkering with it and it gave a great roar as a fountain of blazing gas shot into the air.

The ensuing laughter dissipated any shyness, and I began talking to the men about their work. The coal dust was made into briquettes for home heating. It was a dirty job, 'but someone's got to do it'. Pay, at eighty yuan a month, was above average. Conditions –

Suddenly the men turned away. Someone was shouting at them through a loud-hailer.

'What's up?' I asked.

Nobody replied. The loud-hailer turned its attention to us.

'Go away!'

'That's the boss,' someone whispered. 'He says we shouldn't be talking to you.'

'Why not?'

'Go away! This is a restricted area.'

The men began to retreat. Looking the boss in the eye for a second, I was shocked by the complete hatred on his face. He began haranguing them about 'foreign spies'.

'Let's split,' said Don. 'I don't want any trouble.' He jumped on his bike and rode off.

I took a last look. One or two of the workers were grinning sheepishly, like children getting a telling-off; the rest stared down at the ground. The boss glared at me again. No, it wasn't hate – it was fear.

'He probably had someone on his back,' said Don, once we were out of range. 'That's the way the system works.'

We finally stumbled on the right road out of town, after which we soon reached Estate 12 in new Suzhou – a circular forest of identical apartment blocks. A muddy path led into the centre. We dismounted and wheeled our machines down it, trying to make some sense of the numbering system and wondering why there was nobody about. (Perhaps a man with a megaphone had ordered them all indoors.) Not until we had crossed the entire site did we encounter anyone – a woman, staring at us from the half-finished shop unit in which she had set up a vegetable stall. When we asked her for directions, she eyed us suspiciously, then said she'd fetch 'a friend'. I watched her disappear, and stood fiddling nervously with my bell.

'Sit down,' said Don, squatting on what would be the shop steps if they ever finished the shop. 'Relax.' He scraped around inside the bowl of his pipe, then stuffed it full of shag. 'Look around. It may not be the Great Wall, but it's China. Enjoy it.'

I tried to follow the senior traveller's advice. In front of us was a dirt road with dust devils whirling along it. Then came a stagnant ditch; then allotments – green quilt patches of 'responsibility', sprouting beanpoles, sorghum and young maize. In one of them, two men were hoeing with that swinging peasant work rhythm I had admired so much in Guangdong. Maybe there was a speed of movement which, if struck perfectly, meshed in with the pulse of time itself and lifted the mover out of this world altogether . . .

'Hello!' The woman was back with her friend, and we set off into the wild wood again. Next stop, a Chinese home! But that factory boss was preying on my mind, and I felt only apprehension. What effect would our visit have? 'After the good times, the bad ones will come again' – supposing someone was noting down our movements, so that in the next Cultural Revolution they could haul Mr Wang before a kangaroo court and accuse him of fraternizing with 'foreign spies' . . .

'Don't be so silly,' I said to myself. 'That's history.'

But this was China, where even the human body was mapped differently. And where history wasn't just a series of events but the working-out of an absolute, ineluctable principle. Those border fears came flooding back to me: I was dabbling in matters about which I understood nothing.

'Thirty-seven!' said the friend, stopping under an unnumbered block.

'Thank you,' I replied, and she scurried away. To make her report to the neighbourhood committee?

'Don't get paranoid,' I muttered as we climbed the stairwell, but by now I was praying that there would be no one in.

401, it said on the door.

'That's the one,' said Don. 'You're the Mandarin speaker – see if there's anyone at home.'

I tapped gently, and there was no answer. Don strode up and gave it a thump.

'*Shei a?*' growled someone inside. Who's there?

I was struck dumb.

'Hello?' said Don.

'*Shei a?*' The door opened just enough to reveal an eye.

'Are you M – Mr Wang?' I stuttered.

'Who are you?' the man snapped back.

Don stuck out a hand. 'Don Grizimek. From Sydney.'

'Sy-de-ney?'

'Australia.'

The door flew open: the man (in a vest and denim trousers) was smiling broadly. 'Come in!' he exclaimed. 'Come in!'

So we entered a Chinese home. From a tiny hall with a cracked mirror, a threadbare rug and a picture of the Great Wall lit up in day-glo colours, we went into a bed-sitting room with heavy wooden furniture and plain distempered walls hung with scrolls of calligraphy (traditional, apolitical blessings: 'Long life!' 'Double happiness!'). A group of Chinese, all in denim apart from a young man in a tracksuit and a matt-haired old woman in a black shawl, was sitting on fold-up beds drinking tea.

'Er, *ni hao*,' I said. Their eyes fixed on me. '*Zhe shi*, um, Don.'

'Hi,' said the Australian. He stuck out a hand again, but nobody responded, except by intensifying their stares. Even the young man simply gawped in amazement – one of these bizarre beings, in our house! – and I felt more like a sample under a microscope than ever, squirming with strangeness.

Mr Wang introduced them. All were members of the family, but none of them was Don's friend. 'My son is in Shanghai,' he explained.

'When will he be back?'

'The end of next week, I think. How long are you staying in Suzhou?'

'A few days.'

'Ah. Still, please sit down. Tea?'

Silence fell as he left the room, except for the old woman muttering something about *waiguo ren* (foreigners).

'This room is very nice,' I stammered in Chinese.

'This room is very nice,' the Wangs repeated, as if I were teaching them some weird new language.

'Very nice indeed.'

'Very nice indeed . . .'

'Sydney!' said Don, pointing at a postcard on top of the family TV set. Next to it were two grinning glass tigers in fairground taste. A string of rude comments entered my thoughts.

'Sy-de-ney,' our hosts were saying.

'Australia.'

'Au-da-li-ya.'

Silence returned. My temples began throbbing. Come on, say something! Anything . . .

As the door of Flat 401 closed, Mr Wang was still smiling.

Don shrugged. 'That's travelling – sometimes you hit it off with people, others you don't.'

'But we didn't not hit it off with them,' I replied. 'Not personally. I just couldn't get the words out.'

'That's travelling,' he repeated.

We walked in silence to the foot of the stairs, unlocked our bikes and commenced the slow ride back into town.

'It's all right for you,' I said. 'You've got other contacts. For me, this was a one-off chance – and look what I did with it.'

'Well –'

'I don't seem to be making a very good fist of "travelling". Guangzhou. Hangzhou. Now this . . .'

Don nodded. 'What did you expect?'

'To enjoy myself.'

'What? The moment you arrived?'

'Yes. Why not?'

'That's crazy,' said the Australian. 'That's like picking up a hammer and a chisel and expecting to be able to make a table.'

'I don't see why. Anyway, I did enjoy myself to start off with. That first train ride –'

'Beginner's luck!' he scoffed. 'Travelling's an art. It's not sitting on a beach, it's an activity, a creative activity. So it has to be learnt. Slowly, by experience.'

'I don't see what you mean.'

'You will,' said Don. He paused for a moment, then broke into a smile. 'My teacher used to say: "Don't think of yourself as making a chair, think of it as making you." And it's the same with travelling. It's a craft, with a whole range of pitfalls and rewards that you can only learn by practice. There's no other way. And learning doesn't just mean putting a whole lot of things into your memory – it means changing. Changing who you are, how you do things, how you see things, how you deal with problems and with people and with yourself. Believe me . . .'

He paused, waiting for a comment.

'Yes,' I said.

'I know how you feel,' he went on. 'But getting it wrong's all part of the process. An essential part. You've just got to let it happen. Let China come to you – and it will. Don't expect anything, don't want anything. That's Taoism,' he added.

Taoism? Hidden, absolute power; a frightened woman in a temple; an embarrassing moment of bathos with a tape-recorder . . . Red lights began flashing ahead, and the barrier of a level crossing swung down across our path. A klaxon let out a self-pitying moan: a train came rumbling by. BEIJING, read the boards on the sides of the carriages. God, how I wanted to be on that train, on the move again, bound for a place where I could start afresh, where I might not make such a mess of things.

'Keep the Great Image before your mind, and the Empire will come to you,' continued Don. 'It cannot be seen; it cannot be heard; it is inexhaustible.'

'What is all this?' I cut in. 'What's inexhaustible?'

'The Tao.'

'I haven't a clue what you're talking about.'

He just grinned. 'You will.'

'When?'

'When you're ready.'

That did it. The barrier swung open, and I stamped down on my pedal, to accelerate away from Don and Estate 12 and 'the Empire' and those bloody ornaments and . . . The bike began to move, then a crack rang out like a gunshot as the chain snapped.

Everyone turned to see the pedal swing round and whack me on the achilles tendon, to hear me give a yelp of pain, to watch my bike totter into the side of the road and fall over. A hundred Chinese were roaring with laughter.

Don gave me a hand up. 'That's travelling,' he said with a smile, then pointed to a roadside café just beyond the crossing. 'I fancy a bowl of the local beer. How about you?'

5

Barriers

'So you see,' said Don, 'for the Taoist, will is not an absolute. Not in itself.'

'No,' I replied with a respectful nod.

'It can just be a part of the personality,' he continued. 'A part trying to impose itself on the whole. But only an action proceeding from the whole, natural individual – from the "uncarved block", as Lao Zi calls it – is genuine.'

I pulled out into the middle of the road, to pass a woman with two baskets of rice on a shoulder pole, and a bus blasted its klaxon at me. Serve me right: my mind wasn't on cycling, but on this conversation – one of the many that Don and I had shared over the last few days.

'But in practice,' I replied, 'how do you know if a desire comes from the whole or a part? If you want something, you want it – you can't divide that into bits.'

Don smiled. 'Oh yes, you can. And you do. "Discernment" – remember?'

How could I forget? Of all the stanzas of the *Daodejing*, this one had upset me the most, with its relentless, unworldly logic. Number 16.

I strive to achieve emptiness;
I have stillness – I hold it in my heart.
While the myriad creatures rise in teeming droves
I wait, watching for their return – each to their separate root.

To return to one's root – that is stillness
That is destiny.
To know that destiny is to know the absolute;
To know the absolute is to possess discernment.

To know the absolute – what a precondition for wisdom!

Since our outing to Estate 12, Suzhou had had five inches of rain – and I had learnt a lot about Taoism. The teachings seemed as paradoxical as ever (not least in their influence: the *Daodejing* preached passivity, but its followers had always been the rebels and innovators) but I was beginning to appreciate the wisdom behind their paradoxes. Paradox was a part of life, after all – why not savour it, laugh at it? And then transcend it: beyond the contradictory appearances of everyday life, Taoism promised the same wholeness and fulfilment that Marie-Claude had sought through Zen.

'Religion is not Western-style philosophy,' Don went on. 'It's not a thing that you work out from first principles. It's an education of the spirit, to feel, to know. It's the ultimate craft.'

If it was, then I was still at the stage of trying to hammer a nail and ending up with a bruised thumb. My education – facts and reason, with some neatly ordered culture – seemed more inadequate than ever to the challenge of travelling, to the challenge of China, its ideas, its people, its history . . .

Today, however, who cared? The sun was shining again; we had hired top-quality Flying Pigeon bikes and were riding along a concrete road through the suburbs of Suzhou, destination Lake Tai. The landscape was bizarre and enthralling, as irrational as one of Wei Lang's *Koans* – glowing white tower blocks surrounded by fields of rice and wheat, a line of barges crawling across the horizon like dinosaurs . . .

'Hello!'

The young man pedalled up beside us. I looked away, afraid he might be about to tell us that we were breaking the law by leaving city limits.

'You are from America?' he said instead.

'No,' I replied, smiling with relief. 'I'm from England, and my friend is from Australia.'

'Ah. You are married?'

'Not to each other,' said Don.

'No – you are both male.' The man paused, then asked me my profession.

'Music.'

No grins or renditions of 'Auld Lang Syne', just another 'Ah'.

'What about you?' asked Don.

'I am an engineer.'

'Any special field? Civil, marine, electronic?'

'Ice cream,' he replied.

He noticed the involuntary amusement on our faces, and added that he had studied aeronautics. 'But there are no jobs.'

One could sneer, but there were plenty of people back home doing equally inappropriate work. In music publishing, for example.

'D'you know anything about Taoism?' I asked on impulse.

'No.' He shook his head. 'What are your weekly earnings?'

That was the one trouble with the conversations of the last few days: now I wanted to talk as deeply with a Chinese.

The rock rose slowly out of the heat haze. I was right: there were buildings on top. A pagoda, a pavilion, a tumbledown wall. And lots of trees.

'It's deserted!' I said excitedly. Don just shrugged. When we reached the foot, we found a bus park and a man selling drinks from a corrugated-iron stall. A concrete path, lined with vendors, wound towards the summit. Still, we needed a break. We pulled in and poured two bottles of orange-coloured liquid sugar down our throats before beginning the climb.

As we passed, the vendors clinked their bottles of cold tea to an insistent, mindless beat. The midday sun was hypnotically hot, and a heady smell of camphor came drifting across from the lines of overgrown bushes on the hillside. The roads and rice fields below us soon began to dissolve into an abstract haze of lines and rectangles; the racket of klaxons and motors dimmed to a gentle, contemplative burr. '*Om mani padme hum*,' went the tractors, buses, trucks and bicycles.

Then sharp, new sensations began to fill me. I noticed how fresh the air was. Birds were singing – how few I had heard on the plains! We entered the birch trees just below the walls, and plunged into a bracing rock pool of stippled, yellowish light. Invigorated rather than mesmerized, we reached the summit. A man was sitting by the gateway under a torn umbrella, selling tickets.

'This is Lingyan Shan,' he said, adding that it was an old Buddhist monastery, and that entry was ten fen (two English pence). The four boggle-eyed spirits that guard all Buddhist temples stared down in shock at our ease of entry – or was it in sadness? For beyond them we found a bare stone quadrangle, with red slogans still visible on its walls. In one corner was a crumbling pagoda with empty eye-socket niches. There was no need to ask what had happened, but I did anyway.

'Red Guards,' the ticket man replied. He did a mime of a statue being removed from its plinth and hurled to the ground. The memory of Zhu came flooding back to me with unwanted clarity.

'There's nothing worth seeing here,' I said to Don. 'I can tell. Let's head on for the lake.' At least on the plain, the din and the dust would keep the past at bay. But my companion muttered that we had to 'give the place a chance', and led the way through a second gate – into the most beautiful courtyard I had seen in China. Carved mahogany colonnades ran round the sides: simple, straight columns reaching up into delicate filigree spandrels. Two huge incense cedars stood in the centre, stretching their lower branches out towards each other; at the far end, framed between them, rose a wooden great hall with a roof that flowed like a waterfall. A bright yellow dragon danced along its ridge. Maybe that had scared the Guards away . . .

We walked round the colonnade and up a flight of shallow stairs to the hall, where we peered through tall latticework doors. Dipankara, Sakyamuni and Maitreya, the Buddhas of past, present and future, glowed gold in the half-light, staring out over our heads with total, unshakable impassivity. Their faces were strangely un-Chinese, with their crystal-blue eyes, aquiline noses and pendulous, Easter Island earlobes, even though these gods had been worshipped in the Middle Kingdom for nearly two thousand years (the Han emperor Mingdi had sent messengers to India, after dreaming that a new faith was to be found there).

At their feet knelt an old man in shabby denim, slowly and carefully lighting a vase of joss sticks. He moved with perfect grace, and his lips let out a quiet, undulating chant of prayer. Could anything be less like those miserable, fidgeting penitents in Guangzhou? Everything about him seemed to radiate belief and contentment, and I found myself consumed with envy.

'What's through here?' Maybe Don had seen places like this before; he was pointing at a moon gate, eager to move on. I watched the old man for a moment longer, fixing his image in my mind for use back home, next time somebody started talking about 'success'. Then I followed my friend up a set of stairs – into another complete surprise: a garden. Up here, on a mountaintop, we were surrounded by trees and shrubs: young maples and birches; viburnum, cypress and magnolia in hooped wooden tubs; wild, spreading bushes of rhododendron and fat-budded camellias. Beyond, more stairs led into a formal layout of clipped privet hedges and flowerbeds, centred on a knoll of shapeless pumice on which stood a pavilion in the same dark, dignified wood as the colonnades in the main courtyard. In front of it, a trellis tottered under an enormous, rampant wisteria. At the far end was a sun-facing seat: Don and I saw it at the same moment, and we raced for it.

I won because I wanted to sit there the most. Don was happy to go off and explore, while I sat back and gazed around, gasping at the beauty of this place. Its colours made a mockery of language – how could one word, 'green', cover the brittle mirror leaves of the tea olives, the dingy pine needles and the ebullient new growth on the fruit trees and birches? And what a feeble word 'pink' was for the lone Japanese cherry in one corner, exploding in a firework of blossom. Not to mention 'purple' for this wisteria cascading all around me. Despite all the rival claimants, my attention came to rest on this – in particular on a tendril hanging down by my ear, brushing my shoulder. 'Notice me!' it demanded. So I did.

I had seen wisteria many times before, on suburban houses or in public parks, but never looked at it properly, the way I was looking at this shoot now. In some ways close attention made it uglier: tiny green hairs ran along the stem, and the young leaves were wavy and misshapen. But there was also a power and a delicacy which I had never appreciated. Each leaf was ribbed with veins and subveins, the delta of a miniature river that carried life to every part of it. The tip was coiled up like a spring; it seemed to be quivering with latent energy, on the verge of flinging itself out into empty air and filling the blankness with brightness, change and beauty.

Roquentin came back into my mind, and with him the whole atmosphere of *La Nausée*: brilliant, bitter, teetering on the edge of madness. I thought of a passage where the hero is walking in the park and sees a tree root – properly, for the first time, the way I was seeing this wisteria. He was horrified. The root had no reason to be there: it just was. And by so being, it made a mockery of his search for an orderly, meaningful world. Nature, he decided, is capricious and hostile – man must transcend it; man must subject it to his higher categories of reason and value. How much wiser the nameless monks now appeared, who had created and tended this garden.

'We'll never get to Lake Tai unless we move on,' said Don.

Casting a last look round, I felt both loss and gratitude, as when I said goodbye to Marie-Claude. Then we left, past the dragon-roofed great hall, through the vandalized front yard, to where a fresh stimulus was waiting: the smell of food.

'Won ton?' A matronly woman in a white overall had set up a table and some benches under the temple walls, next to which she was stirring a metal tureen on a primus stove. We sat down and she ladled out two bowls of chewy vegetarian ravioli in thin, salty gravy. They cost ten pence. Some cheap things in China were ludicrously gimcrack (there was a vendor opposite with a selection); others represented disproportionate value.

'More?'

'Yes please.'

The meal left us satisfied but lethargic. So, rather than press on, we followed a path through the birches out on to open mountainside. A warm, flat rock provided the perfect spot to bask. Don took out a reed flute he had bought in Yunnan and began to play; I stared down at the landscape spread out before me – the patterned fields, yellow, green and grey; the square, white villages gleaming in the sunlight; a distant line of blue hills tumbling over the horizon. Jiangsu province, People's Republic of China.

It came without warning or reason: a freak wave of happiness, so extraordinarily beautiful that I couldn't believe it. I made a lurching grab to pull it down and lock it into my heart for ever.

It vanished instantly.

The note was waiting when we returned from our ride: a Mr Wang had called – would we please meet him for dinner the next evening? It gave an address on Yangyu Dajie.

'See what I mean?' said Don. 'Things happen if you let them.'

'When you're ready,' I replied.

But how? Why?

The following evening we wheeled our bikes into a back yard full of overflowing dustbins, and knocked on a peeling grey door. This time, I felt no fear as footsteps approached, the door swung open and a young man strode out and clapped the Australian on the shoulder.

'Don! And your friend. Welcome!'

Wang Weiguo was tidy and eager, wearing neat, round-toed shoes, Terylene trousers and a white shirt a little frayed at the collar. He spoke English slowly but perfectly, forming each word like a work of art, as if to make up for the poverty of his surroundings.

'Please come in.'

The doorway led into a cramped, undecorated hall. A middle-aged woman in a black dress greeted us with a smile. 'My aunt, Wang Jiang,' said Wang. From the kitchen came the smell of spices and the clatter of pans.

'My uncle is preparing the food. He'll join us when everything is ready.'

Wang showed us into the next room – a bed-sit as spartan as the hall. 'Please sit down.' He pointed to a fold-up bed. It was rock-hard.

Don and the two Chinese began talking about Sydney, where Wang had spent three years studying English. I stared round at my new surroundings. They were painfully similar to Flat 401

– the same ponderous furniture; the same calligraphy scrolls on the walls; a detachment of glass animals marching across the mantelpiece, taking the salute from the same postcard of Sydney. Only the dining table looked different. Cut glass glinted in the low-wattage light; the tablecloth was starched and spotless; there were fingerbowls, napkins, carved chopsticks . . . I realized with a shock that this was almost as special a moment for our hosts as it was for us.

'Dinner!' A stocky man with a boxer's nose nudged the door open with a banquet on a huge bamboo tray.

'My uncle Yao,' said Wang.

Yao smiled and picked up the delicate bowls in his big hands, distributing them lovingly around the table: eel in brown sauce; spiced, white Sichuan cabbage; a plate of purple pickled eggs; rice in a big china bowl; crisp segments of fried duck (the smell was delicious). Then he reached out to the glass-fronted cabinet behind him for a bottle of Yantai wine.

'Welcome!' he said, popping it open and filling our glasses. 'To our friends from abroad. Our guests. *Ganbei!*'

'*Ganbei!*' we replied.

We helped ourselves and began to eat. The food was sharp and strange: the eel tender and suffused in the rich, salty sauce; the cabbage tingling as if alive. We consumed it with the concentration and intensity it deserved, pausing only for compliments and more toasts in the sweet, heavy wine: to our home countries, to China, to our travels, to Yao's cooking . . . The warmth of our welcome was as heady as the Yantai, seeping through my feelings and searching out every corner of cynicism and suspicion.

'We are so pleased to have visitors,' said Yao (via Wang: he spoke no English). 'Our government has a new policy – the "open door", we call it. But not many people have chosen to use it yet. Maybe they don't know.'

Don nodded. 'People are still a little scared. But don't worry, they'll be along soon. One day you'll wish you'd never let us all in.'

Yao laughed, then looked serious. 'One of the purposes of the "door" is to enable us to see ourselves from outside,' he said. 'I'm interested to hear what your impressions are of China so far.'

I thought of all the bad memories I had acquired, and filled with shame. Then I thought of the temple and that hillside.

'And please be honest,' our host added.

The Australian broke the silence. 'There's a lot less poverty than in India. And people look happy. People in the West often look bloody miserable.'

'Yes,' I said, leaping in to join him. 'There's so much life in the streets.'

Yao smiled. 'But you must have seen some bad things, too. What about the inefficiency, the pollution?'

Don couldn't hide his surprise.

'For example,' our host continued, 'how long did it take last time you queued for a train ticket?'

'A couple of hours,' said Don. 'But you get used to that on the road –'

'Why? Why should you have to? China gave the world printing, clocks, gunpowder and the compass. Are we incapable of selling railway tickets? Do you have to queue for two hours if you want to catch a train from Sydney to Melbourne?'

Don shook his head.

'Well, there we are. We may still be a Third World country, despite all the progress of the last forty years, but we have First World pride. The West became rich, Japan has become rich – why shouldn't we? There are historical reasons, I know – the stupidity of the late Qing rulers, the civil war, the Cultural Revolution . . .'

He mentioned it! Could I ask? No, of course not.

'Now China wants to catch up. Hence the Four Modernizations policy. Is that enough, that's what I wonder? The real reason why you had to queue for two hours for your ticket was that the ticket clerks couldn't be bothered to serve people quicker. And it's no use "modernizing" industry and making good products, if, when we try to sell them abroad, the sales team is made up of Party officials who want a free holiday. That's the real modernization we need. Our attitude.' He gave a shrug. 'Of course, these are just one man's views. What do our visitors think?'

We scraped the last morsels of food from our bowls and said

nothing, shocked into silence. Yao smiled, and got up to fetch the next course.

'My husband is a long-standing Party member,' said Wang Jiang, the moment he had left the room. 'He joined in 1943, when membership meant danger, not privilege. You mustn't think he's disloyal. Just, well, dissatisfied. Things haven't changed enough for him. Maybe they never could.'

'Do you agree?' asked Don.

She shrugged. 'I take no interest in politics. I want to keep what I have,' she added, gesturing round at their few possessions.

Yao reappeared with a huge bowl of soup.

'Sea vegetables from Lake Tai.' He began ladling out what looked like jellyfish floating in dishwater. 'A local speciality. We should be exporting it all over the world – instead, production is limited by quotas. I had to pull strings to get these. Something I don't like doing,' he added quickly. 'But when you have guests . . .'

Despite its appearance, it was delicious – gentle, like the won ton we had had at Lingyan Shan; a perfect foil to the strong main courses.

Yao showed no disappointment that we hadn't been able to come up with criticisms.

'Anyway,' he said, 'I expect you've questions to ask me about China. Please go ahead. Ask anything you like.'

Anything? I looked at Yao's smashed nose – was that a relic of 1966? I'd have to keep guessing.

'I've always wondered about housing,' Don began.

'And how do people get to join the Party?'

'There must be *some* private property, surely . . .'

'What exactly are these new reforms?'

Our last course, dumplings stuffed with jam, had all gone. It was half past nine – late by Chinese standards. Wang was on his feet making a little speech. Don was trying desperately to compose a reply. It had been a remarkable evening.

Yao filled our goblets with a clear, strong spirit called Maotai. Wang called out the last toast – to friendship. Wang Jiang smiled. The glasses clinked: a universal symbol of conviviality, sharing and openness. One moment on a mountainside had thrown down a hundred barriers between myself and China; now more were falling – more fears, more ignorance.

And this was only a beginning.

We waited, as arranged, at the corner of Renmin Lu and Guanqian Jie, under a huge mural of a young girl sporting the shoulder bag she had bought from the Jiangsu Province Animal By-Products Import/Export Corporation. Across the road, the old lady with whom we had left our bikes stared at us openly. A man pedalled up, parked his Phoenix and paid his three fen. 'Look, foreigners!' she said to him, pointing in our direction. A few people stopped and began staring too. But I didn't care. It was early evening, just after sunset but still softly light. The plane trees along People's Road were coming into leaf; Suzhou's inhabitants were out strolling on the broad, busy pavements. The feeling of well-being was overwhelming.

'He's late,' said Don.

'Maybe he's got held up. He wouldn't cut us, would he?'

'Dunno. Possibly.'

I shook my head vigorously, as if my faith in China depended on our friend keeping the rendezvous we had arranged. His English was so good, he couldn't have got the instructions wrong. And he could hardly miss us – we had now attracted a small crowd.

'Hello!' The slight Australian accent was refreshingly familiar. A few moments later Wang emerged from our spectators, accompanied by a round-faced young woman in jeans and a purple sweater.

'Hello! Sorry – got delayed. Er, this is Miss Wei.'

'Pleased to meet you,' I replied.

Miss Wei turned bright red, mumbled a reply and began staring at the ground. Silence fell.

'So, what's the plan?' asked Don.

'Don't know,' Wang replied. 'I was hoping you'd have some ideas.'

'Do you have films here?' I asked.

'Of course!'

We walked down an alley into a square crammed with rows

of bikes. Six cinemas provided a choice of three Chinese movies, two Soviet ones and Richard Burton in *The Wild Geese*. They were all full.

'How about a drink?' said Don. 'A nice glass of *pijiu*.'

'There aren't bars here,' Wang replied. 'This isn't Australia. The only decent places are for foreign visitors.'

'Come to one with us.'

Wang shook his head. 'Not allowed.'

'That's awful!'

He shrugged. 'That's the way it is. We need the currency.'

'What about, er, the Suzhou Opera?'

'The troupe's on a cultural exchange with America.'

'Earning more currency?'

'No, it costs us money. But we're so proud of it . . .'

At the far corner of the square was a theatre with a brightly lit entrance. There was nothing to indicate what was happening there, so Don and I went in to investigate, followed hesitantly by the two Chinese. Still nothing. The foyer was deserted, but now we could hear music from behind a set of black, padded doors. A bass, a thudding repetitive drum; when Don went over and pushed the doors, a torrent of disco came pouring out.

On the old stage stood a disc jockey in a baggy brown suit and dark glasses, blasting Taiwanese pop through what looked like home-made speakers, while the theatre lights flashed slowly on and off in primary colours. Where an auditorium had once been, there was now a dance floor – empty – round which a few girls and a lot of young men sat at Formica-topped tables drinking orange squash.

Wang was as bemused as we were. 'How long's this place been going?' he asked Miss Wei, who just shrugged. He seemed eager to try it out, and led the way across to a dark, stare-proof corner, where we found a table and sat down. I picked up the menu, wondering if we were somewhere intended for tourists, but it was all in Chinese characters.

'And now, a record by Boney M,' the DJ announced. A few couples took to the floor and started jiggling around out of time.

'Dance?' said Don, half in jest.

Miss Wei looked up and said yes.

'I mean, if that's okay . . .'

'Of course,' said Wang, suddenly relaxed and at ease again, the way he had been at his aunt's. 'Though watch out for the Triads. White man seen with Chinese girl – next morning he's found with a dagger in his back.'

'I didn't mean –'

Our friend burst out laughing.

'Marvellous music!' he commented, once the two had hit the dance floor.

'Yes . . .'

'You don't agree?'

'Well, not really.'

'Artistically, I'm with you. I'd rather take you to a concert of our own "silk and bamboo" music. The silk is the *erhu*, our two-string fiddle; the bamboo a flute of the simplest kind. It's lovely – so delicate, so subtle. But this stuff is loud. You can say anything you like with this going on in the background.'

I shot a residual glance at the salt pot in the middle of the table, then leant forward to listen.

'I'm so glad you met Yao,' said Wang. 'He's a remarkable man. He's either in prison or in high office, depending on the ideological climate. He has strong views, and that's never been a safe characteristic in China. We say that the wise man is like bamboo – when the wind blows, it bends, it doesn't break. But he's not like that. He made going to the West easier for me – not by pulling strings, but by getting me into the right frame of mind. Other Chinese students were shocked by this cult of the individual, this insistence on having one's own view and sticking to it –'

A waitress approached, and he dropped into a series of banal comments about the theatre's Art Deco fittings.

'Of course people do disagree about things in China,' he continued, once she had gone. 'But we try to override these disagreements and get a consensus. Though we don't always succeed. We were killing each other after the Cultural Revolution.'

'Yes.'

'That's not a topic that anyone has mentioned to you, I imagine.'

'No.'

'I thought not.' Wang looked pensive. 'But you'd like them to have?'

'Yes.' On impulse, I told him the story of Zhu, and he nodded sadly. Then the record ended, and the dancers returned to the table.

'Chris and I were talking about the Cultural Revolution,' said Wang. He glanced at Miss Wei, who furrowed her brow but said nothing. 'It's a topic we all try and avoid: I've never discussed it with non-Chinese before. People in Australia asked, but I felt it was disloyal. But you have taken the trouble to visit us: you should learn the truth – good and bad. That's the basis of friendship, after all, isn't it? Honesty. What would you like to hear?'

'Well, your experiences. What really happened?'

Wang leant back in his chair. 'I can only tell you one man's story. There are millions of others, many of them much more dramatic than mine – like that poor teacher of yours. That's what's so awful.'

'I'm sure we'd be interested,' I said weakly.

And our friend began his tale . . .

'Summer 1966. I was at school, aged sixteen. An ordinary student, not particularly interested in politics – you'd be amazed how all these political campaigns just wash over people's heads. One day, there was an announcement: there was going to be a broadcast on TV, so important that we all had to watch it. So we gathered in the assembly room, full of excitement. On came Deputy Supreme Commander Lin Biao and gave a long speech on how important the young were to the future of China, and how we should all read the Thoughts of Chairman Mao and live by them. "So what's new?" we all said; we went back to our lessons grumbling with disappointment and forgot all about it.

'But a month or so later, the first Red Guards arrived at the school. They weren't any older than us, they wore the same clothes, but they were confident and aggressive: young men and women; not children, the way we still were. They made the whole school line up on the sports ground, and lectured us on events in Beijing. "Reactionary elements" under Liu Shaoqi were trying to seize power; to fight back, we had to follow

Chairman Mao and his new campaign, "Down with the Four Olds!" Old culture, old customs, old habits, old – er – there, I can't even remember the fourth one.'

He looked at Miss Wei, who shook her head. 'I was only seven,' she said.

Wang laughed. 'Anyway, after the talk, action. They had taken artefacts from the city temple – books, statues, altarpieces – and got us building a bonfire. Their leader lit it and his colleagues stoked it up with books. "Down with the Four Olds!" we had to shout as each one was thrown on. The *Daodejing*, *Journey to the West* – every classic text went on there. Then he produced a gilded Buddha and said that one of us should throw it. Nobody volunteered – we were all too scared – but the boy behind me pushed me forward. Before I knew what was happening, I was holding this sacred object in my hands, and everyone was shouting at me: "Go on! Burn it!" I was terrified. I froze. The leader looked at me. "Are you against us?" he asked. I shook my head and threw the statue into the flames. Whoosh! It must have been powder dry or rotten or something, 'cause it burnt like paper.'

He paused. 'I stayed away from school for several days after that, pretending to be ill. Finally I had to go in and face the consequences. But there weren't any – of the kind I'd been expecting, anyway. The whole place had changed. The teachers were scared – of me, of everyone. A boy called Zhang had begun organizing "criticism sessions" against them. It was very easy to find "evidence" – a Western book on their shelves, a relative in Taiwan, a landlord somewhere in the family tree . . . Once every teacher had "confessed", we marched them through the streets one Saturday afternoon, in huge pointed hats with slogans on: "I am an enemy of the people" . . . At a kind of rally at the Workers' Stadium, they were lined up and jeered at; we punched them; we made them kowtow to pictures of Mao and sent them on "jet-plane rides" – bending them double for hours, arms up behind their backs. Mr Yu, our geography master, had a heart attack and died. It was a terrible thing. I was there, shouting encouragement, while Zhang and his friends beat these guys up. When Yu rolled forward, we laughed. Even when someone said he was dead . . .'

A silence fell.

'Don't feel you have to go on,' I said.

'No, no. It's important. In the autumn of that year, 1966, there were the big rallies in Beijing – eight in all, I think – in Tiananmen Square. Everyone wanted to go. I wasn't one of Zhang's sidekicks, but – maybe because of that statue – I got the chance. The train was free; we were put up at an army barracks on the outskirts; early next morning, lorries took us back to the centre. The roads were jammed, of course; we marched the last few miles to Tiananmen Square. It's such a special place, that. Mao proclaimed the People's Republic there; it's on our national emblem, on our coins; it's the heart of our nation. To be going there was exciting enough. And with a million others, youngsters like us, from all over China, full of idealism . . . We packed in, and someone began reading passages from the *Red Book* over loudspeakers. We joined in – from memory, of course – waving our books and banners. The more we shouted, the more we seemed to merge into a great, solid mass. We stopped being individuals, with cares and worries and duties – we became part of one huge voice, one great wave of enthusiasm. And that wave built up and up, till Mao himself appeared on Tiananmen. In his army uniform – with a Red Guard armband on. Our armband! The same kind as each one of us was wearing.

'He said a few words in that odd, squeaky voice of his, then drove up and down the square in a jeep, waving his cap. He never came very close to us, but we didn't care. He'd welcomed us all as equals, as fellow fighters. We were all the vanguard of his new, perpetual revolution: we were all going to create a new China, a new world . . . It sounds crazy, but a million teenagers would have died for him that day.'

Our friend gave an embarrassed shrug.

'We were grown-ups from then on, of course. The school closed down – or, rather, became a centre for the study of Mao Zedong thought and military training. That's all we did. Drill, and those texts . . . And there were rallies, too; more "spies" denounced, more vandalism. I remember breaking into the house of a doctor and smashing an altar with a picture of Lao Zi behind it. We hit him with bits of his furniture we'd smashed up – chair legs, bits of an old lacquer table. Luckily he survived: I still see him around the town, walking with a stick – though that's because of his age, not us. But I always cross the road to avoid him.

'Of course, it wasn't long before factions sprang up, each claiming to be the true followers of Mao. Fighting broke out. Just fists at first, then knives, then someone got hold of some guns. Before we knew it, we were in a civil war. Zhang was the leader of an ultra-leftist faction called the Progressive Front. He was killed in a shoot-out with a rival group called May 17th. On Beijie, by the gardens. Then the army stepped in to restore order. Tanks came rolling down Renmin Lu. Some people tried to fight them, but most of us were glad. We were trapped in something we couldn't understand; we could surrender to the PLA without losing face.

'The banishment to the countryside took place after that. We were told we were going to "educate the peasants", though it was really just a ruse to get us out of the way. I think Mao felt almost as helpless as we did – he'd started something he couldn't control, and this was the only way of damping it down again. A column of lorries took us to Anhui, to a mud dormitory on a collective farm near the Huai River, where we spent winter building dykes and summer harvesting grain. Three years' hard labour . . .'

He paused. 'I guess we deserved it. And it wasn't as bad as people in the West make out, anyway. There was a feeling of adventure. I missed my home, of course, but we were young, and everyone else was doing the same, so we didn't feel hard done by. We thought we were doing our duty – to Mao, to the Party, to China.

'In 1971, the universities opened again. I applied straight away. Once that solidarity, that feeling of "all in it together", had been broken, we all wanted to get home as soon as possible. I was accepted: I had a good "class background"; I wanted to study a Western language. They needed translators and interpreters badly, but people were too scared to volunteer: knowledge of foreign languages had only just stopped being a crime. I chose English. Now here I am, talking with you.'

He smiled, then looked gloomy again. 'Of course, I was lucky.

In China we talk about the "lost generation": mine, the people now between thirty and forty. Some people got sent to Xinjiang or Tibet – the death rate was terrible there. Others rotted for seven or eight years in backwaters; when they got back, they were unemployable. Half peasant, half townsman – their elders won't forgive them; their youngers despise them. I saw one of my classmates sweeping the roads the other day. Lin Honghao, a mathematician. I avoided him, too.'

Nobody spoke for a while. The music blasted its way back into our senses.

'The old suffered the most,' Miss Wei said suddenly. 'You did foolish things and you paid the price. But what did they do?'

Wang shook his head. 'We were all victims. We were manipulated, lied to –'

'You can't say that!' she broke in. 'Adults have to take responsibility for their own actions. You can't just blame Mao or the Gang of Four. You'll be a child for the rest of your life . . .'

Wang turned to us. 'You see – it still causes such disagreement.'

Miss Wei began to apologize, but Wang wouldn't have it.

'My friend is right. We've spent too long in China doing what we're told. A nation that just obeys orders, the way we did, isn't ready for democracy, progress or "modernization".' He sighed. 'That's what I really felt when I saw Australia. Not envy or anger, but a terrible fear of all that work to do . . .'

His voice tailed away as if in sadness, but a smile spread across his face. He had done his duty – to his guests, to his country and its new 'open door'; most of all to himself. If there was work to be done, he was better placed to do it now.

'Ah, here comes our order. Shanghai specials: coffee, fruit – and ice cream, too!'

'Ice cream?' said Don. 'That reminds me of this guy we met on the way to Lingyan Shan . . .'

We walked out into the warm night, 'Fernando' by Abba ringing in our ears.

'Thanks for everything,' I said. 'You've given us so much. Hospitality, openness . . .'

'It's been a pleasure,' Wang replied. 'There's so much ignorance about China in the West. People think we're still in the

Mao era, with identical blue denim jackets and identical blue denim brains. But the 1980s have arrived here, too.'

Nevertheless, the cycle attendant stared in unconcealed surprise as two Chinese and two Westerners shook hands warmly and said goodbye. Wang gave a ting on his bell; Miss Wei – we never found out her first name – waved. And then our friends were gone.

Don and I pedalled back through the badly lit streets to our shabby travellers' hotel.

'Hello!' a young pedicab driver shouted as we passed him.

'Looks like we're tourists again,' said Don.

But we both knew he was joking.

6

Under the Taiping Gate

The train let out a long, low groan. I peered out of the window again: Huqiu, Suzhou's leaning tower, had vanished below the scrubby trees – the last visible landmark of a city I hadn't wanted to leave.

'Gotta keep moving,' Don said, noticing my expression. 'Specially with a tight schedule like yours.'

And I had thought two months extravagant.

'We're here for a whole year,' said Maria, sitting opposite us with her friend Elizabeth. Both were students at Nanjing University. 'Imagine that!'

'Yes,' I said wistfully.

'I've got to chalking up little marks above my bed,' she went on, shaking her head and turning her long, red hair into a shivering waterfall. 'It's like prisoners in cartoons – one for each day. Thank God, there's only forty-six more to do. Plus six hours and thirty-five minutes – if the flight leaves on time, which, as it's CAAC, it probably won't. D'you know what I'm going to do when I get back home? Apart from sleep in comfort, eat properly and buy some decent clothes? I'm going to walk round Chinatown staring at everybody, shouting "Hello" and muttering racist insults under my breath. See how you like it, suckers!'

She added a fragile laugh: her natural humour had been pushed to its limit.

Elizabeth's sense of fun had collapsed ages ago. 'I can't think why you backpackers want to visit Nanjing anyway,' she said, spitting out the word 'backpacker' as if it were something revolting she'd eaten. 'It's the most godawful place. Boiling in summer, cold in winter; dirty, smelly, unfriendly.'

'History,' I replied. 'So much has happened there.'

'Killing,' she retorted. 'That's what's happened there. More people have been slaughtered in Nanjing than in any other place on earth. That's probably why it's such a shit-hole.'

'Language, dear,' said Maria, earning a vicious glare from her friend. I realized that they disliked each other almost as much as they disliked China.

'But that's what they believe,' I was saying. 'Marxism, laws of history, determinism . . .'

'Of course, in Taoism –' Don began.

'You and your Taoism!' Maria interrupted.

'Yes, none of the Chinese we've met believe in that sort of thing,' said Elizabeth.

'I thought you said you didn't meet any Chinese,' I replied.

That killed a conversation that had degenerated into a series of monologues anyway. A few minutes later, further embarrassment was saved by the train's pulling into Zhenjiang, where the two students stood up and gathered their bags.

'Next stop on the Magical Mystery Tour,' said Maria. 'I expect we'll dislike it as much as all the others, but you never know. This could be the big one. Have a wonderful time in dear old Nanjing.'

Their seats were taken by two elderly Chinese in Western suits.

'*Ni hao,*' I said.

Neither of them replied.

'Let's have another game of that chess you showed me,' said Don. 'Now those girls have gone, we might actually be able to enjoy something Chinese without being told we're naive, stupid, tasteless, hippies or Communists.'

I had bought a magnetic set while waiting on Suzhou station. I unwrapped it and began setting up the pieces.

'You start,' I said.

Gun to centre three. Damn! I looked up, hoping perhaps that

82

inspiration would leap at me from the poster of the Forbidden City on the wall – and noticed that the men opposite were staring at us.

'You play *xiangqi*!' exclaimed one of them.

'Yes. Would you like a game?'

Five defeats later, we arrived in Nanjing. One of the men, Dr Cao Yuan, handed me a card.

'Please come to my home for dinner on Friday,' he said. He accompanied us through the ticket barrier and flagged down a motorcycle rickshaw.

'Take these foreign friends to the Yangdi Hotel!' he shouted to the driver. Then to us: 'You'll like it there.'

The Yangdi was expensive; its identical concrete rooms were full of gadgets, all of which were 'temporarily out of order'; its restaurant offered exotic-sounding dishes with no detectable taste. But it was in a pleasant suburb, on the 32 bus route – and it had a bar.

'Five yuan on blue!'

A group of American oil executives was sitting in the alcove opposite, staring up at the string of faulty fairy lights by the sign, waiting for one to flash on.

'No, double it – ten on red.'

Zap!

'Ha! Yellow! Banker takes all!'

A Japanese cassette player, lurking among the cans of Tsingtao beer like an opposition footballer in a defensive wall, started to play Laura Branigan's 'Self-Control' for the third time.

'My round,' I said to Don. When I paid, the barman scowled and handed back a note of *renminbi* that had got in among my Foreign Exchange Certificates.

'Bloody stupid system,' I muttered to the man next to me.

'Yeah.' He looked up with a glance of acknowledgement that shocked me with its loneliness.

'Come and join us!' I said impulsively.

'No – I'm . . .'

'Come on.'

'Well, if you . . . Thanks.' He tottered over and collapsed into a chair.

'Not very exciting here, is it?' Don began.

'Exciting?' Our guest was very drunk.

'Yes. D'you know anywhere else we can go? Somewhere a bit, well, more Chinese?'

'More Chinese? Christ, no thanks! I came here to get away from those bastards.'

He began shaking his head, then over-apologizing; finally he sat up straight and held out a hand.

'Let me introduce myself – David Wakebe, student of civil engineering, Nanjing University. Recipient of a Chinese government scholarship – so I can spend a year learning a language I'll never use again; so I can sit through lectures which assume I have the intelligence of a child; so I can suffer racist abuse from giggling Chinese adolescents. Then – if I'm still sane – I can go back home and build railways and world socialism.'

He paused, and looked sadly down at his can. 'Home . . . D'you know, I haven't been out with a woman in two years. Not since I left Africa. If the Chinese see you alone with one of theirs, they'll beat you up – in a gang, of course. All the other African students are male – typical! And the Europeans . . . they're almost as prejudiced as the Chinese, only they're a bit more polite about it. And they've got more money than we have – they can go out and stuff themselves when they can't face another bowl of rice; they can go on weekends to Wuxi or Huangshan. We can't keep up. Anyway, they're not here for so long. One year and they're off home. Blink and you'll miss them. D'you know how long I'm stuck in this bloody place?'

We shook our heads.

'Five years. Five stinking, lonely, underfed, mindless years. I'm not sure I can take it . . .'

He rapped the can on the table, then went quiet again.

'Have you been to that bridge they all go on about?' he asked, after a pause. (Nanjing's two-tier bridge over the Yangzi River was built without any foreign assistance in the 1960s, and the Chinese are fiercely proud of it.) 'It's big, I'll give them that. Over a mile of it. But they've got statues at each end, of people waving guns and sickles and those stupid Red Books. And one of those guys is black. Now there's someone I really feel sorry for. He's here for ever!'

Several Tsingtaos later, the manager threw us out. We walked with David to the main road and hailed a cycle-rickshaw to take him home.

'Take it easy,' said Don.

'Thanks,' replied the young man, collapsing on to the seat.

We watched helplessly as he creaked out of view, then turned for our hotel, via a night snack stall to get some decent food. The faces of our fellow customers – cart-pullers, rickshaw men – looked harsher than usual in the light of the lone, low hurricane lamp: a few yards further on, we passed two down-and-outs lying under a wall. Nobody was paying attention to them: maybe everyone in Nanjing had enough problems of their own.

The museum of the Taiping Rebellion was in an old *yamen* (government office), a walled compound of rambling, single-storey halls linked by corridors and courtyards. Exhibits were strewn randomly around it: dragon-mouthed cannon; pikes made of butchery knives lashed to poles; swords, pitchforks and blunderbusses ... Who would have thought that these antique weapons had conquered half China in the mid-nineteenth century, at a time when the West was building howitzers and ironclads? But they had: the fly-blown campaign maps round the walls told the story, the blue and red lines of Hong Xiuquan's huge irregular armies snaking up from his home base of Guangdong to converge on Nanjing – which the rebels then took with terrible slaughter. Coins of their Heavenly Kingdom testifed to the solidity of their subsequent rule: ten years of it, 1854 to 1864, until foreign intervention destroyed them.

A magnificent bust of Hong stood in the main hall, breathing life into the dusty showcases and wall-charts. Here was a hero; his head held high, his blazing, visionary eyes staring out over us like the Buddhas in Lingyan Shan. Here was a man of the people, in a simple artisan's tunic and a raffish, rock star's bandanna. Most of all, here was a revolutionary, the heir of those peasant emperors Liu Bang and Zhu Yuanzhang, the forerunner of Mao Zedong himself, about to leap down from his plinth and start haranguing me about the abominations of late Qing-dynasty China – daughters sold into concubinage, sons breaking their backs to pay rents and taxes . . .

'He was mad, wasn't he?' said Don.

'I don't know,' I replied.

Hong was born into poverty, the son of a farmer. But he was bright – clever enough to enter for China's élite civil-service exams. However, his background told against him, and he failed. He took this failure with an intense, self-destructive bitterness, falling into a fever from which he appeared to be dying. At the height of the illness, he had a vision of an old man handing him a sword and a young man swearing on it to be his blood brother. Although he didn't understand what it meant, the vision rekindled his pride, and he recovered.

Hong appeared to accept his fate, and took a job as a village schoolteacher. It was poorly paid, but a small step up the social ladder. But in private he was still brooding on the meaning of that vision. One day, when he was on a visit to Guangzhou, a Christian missionary handed him a pamphlet in the street. He stuffed it in his pocket and forgot all about it; only later did he dig it out and read idly through it – and understood, in a flash: the old man of his dream was the Christian God; the younger man was Jesus. Together they were commanding him to rise against the Manchu and found a new dynasty.

Hong began preaching his new gospel at once. He was to set up a 'heavenly kingdom' (*taiping tianguo*) on earth. Idols – the temples of China's other religions – were to be destroyed. Political power was to be seized by insurrection. His Society of God-Worshippers grew fast, attracting converts from landless peasants, coolies and army deserters – desperate, demoralized men, whom Hong formed into disciplined guerrilla units. Attacks were launched on Qing garrisons in Guangdong and Jiangxi – almost always successful. With each victory, Hong's forces swelled; in 1852 he began his march north, with a million men, according to some sources. That extraordinary expedition ended here, in Nanjing – or Tianjing, as they renamed it, the Heavenly Capital – from which the village teacher ruled half China.

I looked up at the statue again. As 'heavenly king', Hong instituted a series of intelligent, liberal reforms: combating the opium trade, banning foot-binding, returning property seized by tax-farmers and usurers to the men who worked it. If the Manchus hadn't swallowed their xenophobia and allied themselves with Westerners, his Yongan dynasty might have thrived, mellowed and prospered. But instead his huge southern empire crumbled before superior military technology. By 1864, the combined Qing and foreign 'ever victorious army' was at the gates of the Heavenly Capital, bombarding it from land and water. The second massacre in a decade followed Tianjing's fall, and a hundred thousand citizens were killed, including Hong. However worthy its aims, his rebellion achieved nothing lasting – and is generally reckoned to have cost the lives of twenty million people.

We left Hong Xiuquan to his dreams, and walked out to the museum garden. It was a pretty place – a pool surrounded by twirling pumice and languorous, grey bamboo – but my mind was not on beauty. Elizabeth had been right: Nanjing must have seen more bloodshed than anywhere else on earth. The old woman who poured us a ten-fen cup of tea straight from the kettle must have lived through the Rape of 1937, when the Japanese stormed into the feebly defended town and butchered a quarter of a million inhabitants. Ten years earlier, the Yuhuatai massacre had seen truckloads of Communist suspects taken out to the southern hills and gunned down. (The massacre might even have been planned here, in this garden: the old *yamen* had been headquarters for the Guomindang secret police.) Then, of course, there was 1949 – another siege, another capture, no doubt scores to settle . . .

'Another cup?' Don suggested.

'No. This place gives me the creeps.'

We rode out to the city walls, to the Taiping Gate, and stood beneath them. Don began to intone a liturgy of facts and figures from a guidebook: these were the largest city fortifications in the world; they were twenty feet thick, forty feet high, fifty kilometres long; they were six hundred years old. He needn't have bothered: nothing matched the immediate physical experience of this great rockface of damp, black stone. It seemed to radiate violence like a smell – sieges, massacres, rapes and rebellions on a scale unimaginable in Europe until this century.

The man who had ordered its construction was Hongwu, the founder of the Ming dynasty. 'Grab power by force; rule by terror.' On his accession, he had put a hundred thousand enemies to death. Yet still he felt the need to build this wall – or rather to get an army of slaves to do it for him. Safe behind it, he had set about creating a totalitarian state.

A great gloom came over me, as irrational and as intense as the joy I had felt on Lingyan Shan (though much less fleeting). Men who had renounced the world could tend trees on safe, quiet hillsides, but affairs on the plains followed different rules. These rules were embodied in these dismal walls and their dismal history – rules of war; rules not of the jungle but of the savannah, of the open lands for which mankind's common ancestors had fought endless tribal conflicts. Under these conditions – the ones that, surely, had formed our nature – the individual has no chance of survival outside the group to which he or she surrenders their loyalty. Wasn't this our real essence: Nanjing Man, a unit in perpetual mass combat?

I thought of my wisteria shoot, and sighed. Life was a miraculous gift, but it committed the recipient to a lifetime of struggle and suffering. The Buddha, I remembered, had understood this and made it the cornerstone of his philosophy: those mountaintop monks should have been punished for heresy.

Marx had understood too.

Marxism was one of those midnight answers to the world's problems, and to see it in action was one of my reasons for coming to China. Were its claims true? Did it work? Every hotel lobby had its carefully stocked shelf of *China Reconstructs* and *Beijing Review*, bristling with evidence for a positive answer to these questions. Impressive evidence, too. Life expectancy in the People's Republic had almost doubled since 1949, from a miserable thirty-five to sixty-eight, only a few years behind the richest countries in the world. Literacy had risen from 20 to 78 per cent. Since 1980, real GNP had more than doubled. Standing in a Chinese street, watching these busy, lively people flowing past on their bikes, I felt anger at the West's automatic equation of 'Communist' with 'bad'. Just think of all the extra

years these people would have to live. But there was another
side to Marxism, an apocalyptic, ideological side, to which life
expectancies and GNP were irrelevant. It was a side I had always
looked on with great scepticism – until now, here in the shadow
of these walls.

Marxism isn't just a recipe for kick-starting moribund econo-
mies; it is a theory of man and a theory of society that purports
to explain everything about the world we live in (and its past and
its future). It is, in effect, a religion. Its god is history, an ineluctable force driving the development of human society through
a series of inevitable stages (primitive, slave-owning, feudal,
capitalist, Communist). The motor for this development is not
original thought, experimentation or liberal humanitarianism,
but violence – a perpetual struggle between classes until the last
oppressors (capitalists) are destroyed. The role of the individual
in this process is utterly trivial. Our daily actions have no effect
on anything that matters (except when they further the ends
of history). Our private values have no grounding in absolute
reality, being simply products of a temporary ideological super-
structure. Only the vast, machine-like process is real, and only
those who understand it and march with it can have any genuine
wisdom or dignity.

It sounded crazy, yet what use had personal virtues or values
been to the inhabitants of Nanjing in 1937, or 1927, or 1864? One
squeeze of a Japanese trigger could end a whole life of kindness and
humanity; only a mass, violent response was effective and meaningful. I thought of Wang in Tiananmen Square: maybe his ecstatic,
communal enthusiasm hadn't been so artificial after all. I thought
of the China I imagined myself to have discovered – the quirky,
warm China of 'Jingle Bells' and 'Moon River', chess games and
animal impressions; the 'open door' that had let us into a feast. It
all suddenly seemed an irrelevance, a flower of my own sentimental
imagination. This was reality – this wall in front of me.

'Is there anywhere in Nanjing not connected with killing
people?' said Don suddenly.

I looked through the guide. 'No.' But then perhaps there
shouldn't be.

'I fancy a *pijiu*,' he went on. 'Somewhere nice.'

*

89

We both knew it was wrong the moment we arrived, but some kind of magnetism drew us in; maybe the same force that glued a line of gawping peasants to the forecourt railings of the Jinling, Nanjing's newest, most luxurious joint venture hotel. We swept through the gates on our tatty bikes and hid them behind a tub of palm trees; we tried to sneak in past the braided doorman, but he noticed us and bowed obsequiously.

'Good afternoon, sir.'

We might be scruffy but we were Western. We belonged. This was our answer to the earthy mass realism of Marx and Mao – individual choice. Muzak. Bellhops padding across the marble lobby like gelded cats. A group-tourist with a paunch arguing with a commissionaire about having to share a bathroom. A febrile, selfish, unreal answer – doomed because it wasn't worth fighting for.

I rode into town alone, stopping to wander into a market where stallholders were selling cheap, colourful goods.

'Hello!' Purple acrylic sweaters, tracksuits and Taiwanese pop cassettes. In Suzhou, side streets had been cheerful places, full of banter and bustle. Forget the tourist sites, forget history. Meet the people! I exchanged grins with a middle-aged man as I stopped to flick through his barrowload of Shanghainese jeans, all about eight sizes too small. A small crowd gathered to stare. I heard a laugh – a jolly, personal response to one of life's absurdities. Then a sharp, angry voice joined with it.

'Yah! Big-nose!'

The speaker was pointing at me. When he saw that he had attracted my attention, he shouted another insult. The crowd began to titter: I shrugged and moved on to the next stall.

'*Yang guizi!*' He walked towards me, stopping a few feet away and fixing me with a look of mindless, meaningless fury.

I had to face him. 'What's the problem?' I asked, hoping my Mandarin would embarrass him into silence.

He replied with a stream of Nanjing dialect, whose content I would have to guess.

My own anger flared up for a second; then I turned away

into the crowd, back to my bike. The wise general, wrote Sun
Zi, is never provoked. The ranting vanished into the hubbub
of a Chinese market. I clicked my back-wheel lock open with
a steady hand and gave my bell a chirpy ting as I rode off.
One man among millions, and he looked a bit crazy, anyway.
I was in Nanjing, one of the world's most historical cities, and
determined to enjoy it.

Suddenly he was there in front of me, cursing and gesticulat-
ing. 'You smell of cow!'

I looked round for another way out, but there was none.
People were beginning to turn, to watch and laugh.

'Go back to your Western cow stall!'

Of course – the Jinling! How would I feel if there were such
a hotel in my own country, reserved for an alien, plutocratic
race? If I had to work all day in a factory or a rice field, while
these intruders were perpetually idle? But the man had started
advancing towards me, and my sympathy died at once. I had
to get away, and there was only one method of doing that: to
ride straight at him, so that he'd have to jump clear or get a
set of handlebars in the abdomen. I stamped on the pedal and
shouted at him to move. He spat and stood his ground. The
cycle rattled in complaint; my legs pumped; now he was only
a few feet away . . . Suddenly I felt a horrible elation. I didn't
want him to move – I wanted to smash into him, to make him
double up in pain and crash to the pavement. I wanted him to
know that not only Chinese hate to lose face; that I might be
ugly, weird and outnumbered, but I could fight as hard and as
bitterly as he chose; that if life was about struggle and violence,
then I could be a savannah animal too . . .

At the last possible moment, and without conscious thought,
I jinked round him.

'Self-preservation!' I said to myself, looking at the clear road
ahead. 'What a marvellous instinct!' But the bike began to slow
down: he had grabbed hold of the rack and was pulling at it.
Cowardice, that was what my marvellous instinct had been. In
fear, now, I brought my fist down on to his hand – too soft: my
assailant grinned and held fast, daring me to do it again. Coward!
Instead I launched a full-force punch at his chest. It connected:
the man staggered back and let go. The crowd, which had been

laughing, fell silent. Had I misunderstood? Maybe he had been joking? The hell he had. I had a few seconds to accelerate away, before the spectators focused their new-found anger on me. It was just enough.

'Well, you get yobbos in every country,' said Don, as we sat in the safety of the Yangdi bar. 'You mustn't let that kind of thing get to you. Have another of these Yangzi Bridge beers.'

'It's not just one guy. They were all rooting for him. They'd have lynched me –'

'You got away.'

'Just. Anyway, it's not China. It's me, too. I've never felt quite like that about anyone before. I really wanted to hurt him.'

'So you've learnt something about yourself. Everyone does on the road.'

Don went and brought the beers, while I sat and brooded. Laura Branigan was still singing in the background, panicking about her loss of 'self-control'. (When I got home, I'd send the hotel another tape.)

'I'm leaving,' I said when he got back. 'I hate this town. Tomorrow morning, I'm going to the station to book the first ticket I can. Soft, hard, I don't give a damn.'

'You can't do that!' Don looked horrified.

'Why not?'

'Tomorrow's Friday. You can't let our chess-playing doctor down.'

'Yes, I can. I've had enough of Nanjing.'

Bullets of tropical rain ricocheted off the tin roofs of the roadside shops. The wind had blown my West Lake umbrella inside out ages ago: by the time we reached our destination, we were drenched. And lost – the map that Dr Cao Yuan had drawn for us bore no relation to the reality of Nanjing's back streets.

'Excuse me,' I began, but the animated plastic sheet that I had addressed sploshed past without a word. I held the card out to a snack-stall owner: he snatched it and eyed it suspiciously.

'Who's this?'

'None of your business.' I grabbed it back. A taxi driver pulled up, hoping for a fare, took one look at our sodden clothes and drove on.

'Let's try here,' said Don. We waded down a flooded road, and ended up knocking at a black, unmarked door that might have been number 24. It wasn't: a man in a dressing gown answered. He looked only mildly surprised, as if rain-soaked Westerners frequently turned up on his doorstep.

'Come in.'

Once we were inside, Don showed him the card.

'Dr Cao Yuan? Anyone know him?' The man handed the card to his wife and teenage son, who were watching volley-ball on a black-and-white TV. 'No? Honglin, go and ask the neighbours.'

We protested feebly as the boy put on a kagoule and headed out into the rain, as his wife vanished into the kitchen to make us tea, as he insisted that we sat and dripped on to his best sofa in front of his one-bar electric fire.

'Nanjing is known as one of the three furnaces of China,' he said with a laugh.

'Come in! Come in! All of you.'

Two of us obeyed instantly, but the boy – who had insisted on accompanying us in case we got lost – shook his head and said he should be getting home. 'It is my duty to help foreign friends,' he added in reply to our thanks, then turned on his heels and disappeared into the storm.

'We were getting so worried,' Dr Cao continued. 'Oh, your shoes!'

Cao's wife looked even more nervous than he did. She wag-gled her head with concern as she showed us into the tiniest bed-sit I had ever seen.

'Sit down, please. You must.'

'We're so wet,' I replied, but she was as insistent as our last host had been.

'Doesn't matter. Make yourselves comfortable, that's the main thing. You want to watch TV?' She flicked it on before we could answer; the screen seemed to balloon out at us and fill half the room. 'You want some sweets? Tea?'

We settled down to watch a film about the 1930s. Mrs Cao

explained the plot: the heroine had been married off by her parents to a loutish Guomindang soldier and now she had met a handsome young man who was an underground Communist activist. The girl was just about to find herself alone with the activist for the first time – when Cao put his head round the door and announced dinner.

'I think they fall in love,' said Don.

Plates of food lay steaming in wait on the table: rice, vegetables, salted duck (a local speciality), eggs. And wine, in goblets.

'*Ganbei!*' said Cao. The magic summons to good will and friendship.

'*Ganbei!*' we replied – and the spirit of Suzhou arose at once, mingling with the steam and the smell of soya sauce, making all the negative thoughts that had filled my mind in this city seem as artificial as the celluloid drama we had just been watching. This was reality, to talk of everyday matters – families, workplaces and life styles; personal struggles and individual achievements. Politics went unmentioned, and when I broached the subject of history, the doctor shook his head.

'Yes, Nanjing's story is one of terrible violence. My father was killed in 1936. I still don't buy Japanese goods. But history is history. We have a teenage son.' (He was away at college, but I had peeped into his room: football posters from all round the world – Maradona, Pelé, Ian Rush . . .) 'We don't want him to share our anger. Now we have the chance, we want to get on with our lives in peace.'

'People have always wanted that, though,' I said hesitantly.

'But we have the means to achieve it. Technology to create wealth. Medicine to remove sickness. Education – the most important of all – to remove ignorance. Confucius taught us the value of that, two thousand five hundred years ago. Have you read him? No? You should. He understood the purpose of the past, that it is there to be learnt from, to create a better future.' Cao raised his glass in another toast. 'To the future! *Ganbei!*'

'*Ganbei!*'

After dinner, we played *xiangqi*, a master class for two eager beginners. Then it was time to go. Rain was still bucketing down, as if the sky were crying itself out for the victims of history.

Although we asked him not to, the doctor insisted on donning a leaky mac and accompanying us to the bus stop.

'We'll be okay.'

'Please, you'll get soaked.'

'No – you must catch the right bus!'

When a 32 pulled up (with the standard, unmissable Western numerals on the front), our host shook us warmly by the hands, then pulled a paper bag out from under his mac. Inside were two chess sets.

'So you will have good memories of Nanjing,' he said.

Nobody else was checking in or out, so the receptionist left his desk to join me on the hotel steps.

'To which city are you going?' he asked.

'Qufu,' I replied.

'Ah! Birthplace of Confucius. Great Chinese philosopher.'

I had been surprised when Dr Cao talked about 'the Sage' with such respect; now this man – in his twenties – was doing the same. 'I thought he was out of date,' I said. 'Wasn't he criticized in the Seventies?'

The receptionist shrugged. 'So was everybody. Now we respect him as a great thinker in Chinese history. You are interested in history?'

'No.'

He looked hurt.

'I mean yes. In a way.'

Before the young man could ask what I meant, Don appeared in a taxi that he had conjured up for me. He helped me put my luggage into the boot and we stood shaking hands. From Nanjing my friend was heading west, via Xi'an and the old Silk Road to Kashgar. I would miss him.

'Enjoy your travelling!' he said, as I got in.

'Yes. I will.' It was a promise.

We took a back route to the station. 'Much quicker,' the driver said. I had heard that one before, but now I didn't care; if we went a long way, I'd see more of Nanjing. We disappeared down a dirty alleyway, swinging round a corner into a street blocked by a crowd of teenage boys. The driver hooted at them to get out of the way; they jeered. As we began barging through them, they looked in and began swearing.

'*Yang guizi!*'

The driver gave a blast on his horn and forged on. 'Very silly people,' he said, once we were in the open again.

'We have them in England, too,' I said with regret.

He nodded. 'All over the world, I think.'

All over the world . . . Perhaps that was what I had come travelling for – to realize that if there were absolute truths about life, they were within us, not outside. And that history did not force men to be cruel – we always had a choice. And that this freedom made individual gestures of kindness, trust and welcome, of the sort I had received from many Chinese on my journey, into things of immense, absolute worth.

7

The Sea of Tranquillity

The red rear lamp of the Nanjing–Tianjin express swayed off into the night. I was alone! In Shandong province, in the Chinese countryside – in the world that until now I had only stared at through train windows or conjured up in daydreams. 'When I get to Qufu . . .' I had told myself, and now I was here (or almost: this was Yanzhou, the nearest point that the Confucian priests had allowed the noisy, fire-spitting railway).

The last clatter of the express's wheels died away and the lamp swung out of view. A delicious silence descended, as rich as loam, as expansive as the Chinese plain.

'Hey!' An official was waving at me. 'What are you doing?'

'Nothing.' I showed him my ticket, and he scowled.

'You should leave the platform immediately you disembark.'

'It's beautiful here.'

He looked at me as if I were mad. 'Those are the rules. Go away.'

Yanzhou had one hotel, tall and characterless, with a scrum of angry travellers besieging the reception desk. I joined them, but didn't have the spirit for a fight. I had come here to relax, to unwind, to 'let China come to me'.

I was served last of all. 'This place is for citizens of the People's Republic only,' said the clerk.

'But there aren't any other hotels in this town.'

'Correct. You are on your way to Qufu?'

'Yes.'

'You should go there tonight.'

'It's past midnight!' I stood my ground and glared at him; he pretended I wasn't there. I was just about to give up when he began scribbling on a piece of paper.

'Room 17, tenth floor.'

'Thanks.' I picked up my pack and walked over to the lift.

'Out of order,' said the clerk with a smirk. One all . . .

My room was tiny and mildewed, with a bare bulb, a hard wooden bed – and a Panda television set in one corner. I wiggled the little wheel that took me through the channels – two national, one local – past a Japanese police thriller, more volleyball and a programme about cow disease. Then I went and washed in a kind of communal trough down the corridor. The lavatory was a row of holes, over which other late arrivals squatted, reading newspapers.

'I can't,' I muttered, but my bowels insisted. Trying to hide my embarrassment, I loosened my trousers and squatted down too. The man next to me began to stare – not at me, but at my square box of soft toilet paper.

'Try some,' I said.

He took a leaf, rubbed it between his finger and thumb, and put it into his shirt pocket.

It was time for bed. I was soon drifting down a replay of Nanjing's Yangzi bridge and the reddening fields of northern Jiangsu, when a couple began arguing outside my door.

'It's quarter to one!' I muttered irritably. I got up and asked them to keep quiet. They nodded sheepishly and retired to their room – next door, where they resumed the discussion. Someone across the corridor put on a cassette of Taiwanese disco; a bus driver in the square outside began tooting his horn. 'Qufu!' shouted the conductor. Soon after the bus had roared off – it needed a new exhaust – a goods train came rumbling into Yanzhou station. Railwaymen began uncoupling trucks, hammering at the links with crowbars and sending the wagons clanking and crashing into sidings. Upstairs, a baby awoke in strange surroundings and wanted reassurance.

It wasn't till after four that quiet descended. At five thirty, the factory across the square began its morning broadcast of martial music.

*

The driver blasted his klaxon at a cycle-cart and revved up to overtake it, making the whole bus shake. The man next to me turned his cassette player up a notch. Another cycle-cart; another mad, mechanical bray. When this ride was over, I'd sit back and relax to some nice, soothing heavy metal.

We were entering a town, a makeshift, dusty place. Its main road was lined with corrugated-iron workshops and squat, half-finished concrete apartment blocks with wires sticking out of the uprights.

'Is this Qufu?' I said to my neighbour.

'Eh?'

'*Is this Qufu?*'

'Yes.'

We jolted into a yard full of windowless, rusting buses, and were surrounded by touts even before we had stopped. The Chinese passengers disembarked unnoticed; the one magnetic Westerner was hounded across the yard and out into the street.

'Hotel?'

'Change money?'

'Rickshaw?' One rider began pedalling along beside me, trilling his bell.

'Old city – long way!' he shouted. Ring ring ring . . .

'Not by my map.'

'Your map's no good!'

I walked on.

'One yuan – cheap!' Ring ring ring . . .

That bell was tolling in mourning for a still-born dream – my fantasy of a great, timeless sea of tranquillity, waiting out here for me in Shandong province.

Ring ring ring. 'Ninety fen! Eighty!'

'Oh, all right.'

It was my first ride on a rickshaw, perched on its clammy vinyl seat above the wobbling back wheels. My pack jiggled contentedly beside me; the head of the rider bobbed up and down in time to the rise and fall of the pedals. Local people watched with amusement. In big cities, rickshaw men pulling foreigners were often abused for acting out subservient, colonial roles; here everyone knew who was exploiting whom. We travelled at least a hundred yards, to a crimson archway at the mouth of a silent, cobbled alley, at the far end of which stood a set of gorgeous red gates.

'Old city!' said the man, coasting to a halt and mopping his brow in mock exhaustion. 'D'you want a good hotel?'

'No thanks, I've got one already.'

He reached for the bell again, but there was something about this place that stilled even him. The spirit of the Sage, perhaps? We were at the bottom of Queli Jie, where, two thousand five hundred years ago, Confucius had lived.

I watched the rickshaw rattle off in search of further prey, then stood pondering this quiet street and its famous inhabitant. Kong Fuzi, Father Ni, 'Learned Sage of Moral Excellence', 'First Master of Princely Accomplishment'. . . Everything I had read about this man conspired to make me dislike him and his timorous, priggish, servile, misogynistic philosophy. Enquiry and speculation meant nothing to him; science was vulgar and religion pointless. Creativity was equally unimportant. The only good culture was old culture: study the classics, don't waste time making anything new. Convenience, order, convention and obedience were the cornerstones of his tight, neurotic universe. Yet he had claimed to know the secrets of human society, to know what made the unruliest men law-abiding and fair. And China had built its civilization on his teachings.

The gates at the end of the street belonged to the mansion of Confucius' descendants, the Yansheng dukes. Part of it – the servants' quarters – had been converted into a travellers' hostel. It had sounded so good in the guidebook that I had got Wang to write for me, reserving a room.

'Hello.'

The clerk looked up from his martial-arts magazine with an expression of irritation.

'I've a room booked. Mr West.'

He leafed through a leather-bound ledger and shook his head.

'*Meiyou.*'

'But you must have. I wrote from Suzhou, over a week ago.'

He searched again, running his finger down the pages and

muttering '*Meiyou*' over and over again. Through the doorway, I could see a sunlit courtyard surrounded by low white buildings, with two perfect round moon gates and a tiny pleasure garden of bonsai trees and pumice – and all for travellers, not tour groups.

'*Meiyou*.' He shut the book. I tried the stand-and-glare technique, but my opponent was a seasoned campaigner, entrenching himself behind the magazine and ignoring me utterly. Picking up my pack, I turned for the door.

'You don't have any rooms vacant, I suppose?' I said, halfway out. It sounded silly, but I hadn't actually asked directly.

'Oh, yes. Plenty. What do you want? Single? Double?'

Qufu's Drum Tower was part of a defensive wall – but this was Shandong, not Nanjing. Bunting fluttered from its parapet, and the red banner sagging across its central archway welcomed tourists to the city. If it testified to absolute laws, they were of beauty, not history: its grey stone sides tapered gently, commanding the eye to follow them to the top, where a bright, delicate pavilion glowed vermilion, emerald, gold and turquoise in the late-afternoon sun. I stood staring up at this totally unexpected treasure, waiting to get bored, to have seen enough, to spot some flaw – and couldn't move.

'Confucius forest, five yuan!' In the end it was a rickshaw man that budged me.

I dived down a bumpy, narrow path to get away, and was in countryside almost at once, on the mud main street in a village of thatched one-storey houses. Tiny alleyways led off left and right, blocked by cows, hay bales or rusting machinery. Two mandarin geese began waddling along in front of me, waggling their outsize bottoms and honking: 'Foreigner coming!' Their call brought urchins to the roadside, to stare and shout.

'Hello!' Absurd, instinctive happiness radiated from the faces of these ragged children. Why hadn't crotchety old Confucius come walking here, to see smiles like these? Then I was out in open country, in a sunken lane between sunlit wheat fields. A delicious feeling of space and adventure filled me – my 'timeless sea' was a reality after all. And a brick enclosure was beginning to appear over its horizon, with yew trees and orange-tiled roofs.

A temple! I quickened my pace, but by the time I reached the entrance, its massive wooden doors had been padlocked shut. Whatever was in there, I would have to wait to discover.

It was dark when I got back to Qufu. The town had dissolved into a series of fragmentary impressions, into shadows, smells and sounds. Pots clattered in a cheap restaurant; radios wailed out of Chinese-only hotel windows; a horse-drawn tonga cart came clopping towards me. Then I was back on Queli Jie, between its high walls and sentinel lines of locust trees – safe from all intrusion, surrounded at last by the wholeness and perfection of silence.

'The Still is Lord of the Restless,' Lao Zi had written.

'*Waaaa!*'

The plastic trumpet was a few inches from my ear. Not much further beyond it, a guide's megaphone began feeding back. A bus was tooting its horn furiously at the bottom of the road. Qufu had been invaded overnight, caught in a surprise attack – just as Sun Zi advocates – and thus overrun without resistance.

'Hello!' shouted a teenager in dark glasses and a hat with an inflatable tiger's head on.

'Hello!' shouted a man in a T-shirt with HAPPY TEAM across the front.

'Hello!' shouted a child swinging an acrylic panda by its one remaining ear.

'Hello!' The last voice appeared to come from a picture of Confucius with a neat round hole where his head should have been. Then a face appeared in the hole. 'You want photo?' it shouted. Instant sagehood – the rest of Qufu seemed to have gone crazy; why shouldn't I? But before I could reach him, a fat, bespectacled man waddled into my path and stuck out a hand.

'How do you do!' he said, grinning.

'Oh – hello.'

'I am Zhuang Boling, student of English!'

'Ah.' I introduced myself, answered a few standard questions (age, nationality, marital status), then commented on the number of visitors.

'It's May the first!' Zhuang exclaimed. He looked at me, suddenly full of pity. 'You do not get proper holidays in England?'

'Well, of course, but –'

'In the People's Republic, we have seven days' public holiday every year! January the first, three days at Spring Festival, International Labour Day, Army Day and National Day.'

'Really?'

'And there are holidays for women and minors. International Working Woman's Day, Chinese Youth Day and International Children's Day.'

'That's interesting.'

'Workers of grade three get extra holiday. Higher grades can get up to three weeks a year.'

'Oh.'

'What is your grade?'

'I don't think I've got one. Not very high . . .'

He looked puzzled. No grade? Next I'd be saying I didn't belong to a work unit.

'Our factory is involved in processing of dangerous chemicals,' he continued instead. 'We have third best safety record in Shandong province. Last year only two accidents involving injury, and one spillage.'

'I'm glad,' I replied. I'd hate the thought of this chirpy fellow – the Michelin man, that was whom he reminded me of – stepping in a puddle of acid and popping. But I also felt relief when his purple-strapped digital watch began to play 'Yellow Submarine', and he said he had to rejoin his group at the Confucius temple. I had come to Shandong to be quiet . . .

'Please enjoy stay in our province!' said Zhuang, and bobbed off into the crowd.

We rode east out of the town, my new roommate and I – on the last two bikes from the Confucius bike-hire company (other travellers had seen the May Day invasion coming).

'It should be here,' I muttered as we coasted to a halt. We scanned the horizon for one of China's few pyramidical tombs (of Shao Hao, a semi-mythical ruler of four thousand years ago). A distant line of trees; a sandstone knoll half covered with grass;

broad, flat fields of young wheat waving in the wind – but no pyramid.

'Typical China,' said Brett. 'Nothing where you expect it.'

'No. Well, that's travelling.'

'It certainly is.'

'Hello!' A truck roared past with a blast on its klaxon and a wave from the workmen on the back.

'I hate it,' said Brett.

'What?'

'Travelling.'

We rode a bit further, then gave up the search, returning home – on my suggestion – cross-country.

'Travelling's an art,' I began hesitantly, as we bumped along a path that seemed to be growing narrower every moment. 'It takes time to learn. Let China come to you, that's what you've got to do.'

'I don't see what you mean.'

'Well, you mustn't expect too much, too soon. You have to let things happen. They do – when you're ready. Believe me. That's Taoism,' I added cheerily.

'Taoism?' His face puckered in contempt. 'You don't believe all that stuff, do you? Look at the state of their country! Look where it's got them!'

A village came into view, and, just before it, a walled enclosure like the one I had seen last night. We rode up to it and parked our bikes in an empty rack. A man was sitting by the entrance selling tickets.

'Is this the tomb of Shao Hao?' I asked him.

'Yes,' he replied, surprised that we needed to ask.

'See what I mean?' I said to Brett. 'Things happen.'

'Coincidence,' he muttered.

We hadn't spotted the Great Pyramid of Qufu from the road because it was only fifteen feet high. But it was of white marble that glowed in the afternoon sun, and behind it rose a hillock of grasses and ragwort, where we lay on our backs and stared up at the stunning azure blue of the sky. I had never seen blue so deep and pure. Was it the latitude, or the distance from cities? Or something that had changed in me, the perceiver?

Brett took out a Walkman and put it on. A mindless beat

and a strangulated wail squirted into the air like a swarm of angry bees.

'Please turn that off,' I said.

'What?'

'*Turn it off!*'

He was so shocked that he complied.

'This is a tomb,' I continued. 'Respect for the dead is particularly important in China.'

'There's no one around. Anyway, I'm bored.'

'Bored?'

'Yes, bored. B-o-r-e-d. When you said pyramid, I thought you meant something big. Like Egypt. This thing is pathetic.' He stood up. 'I think I'll go back to the hotel.'

He paused, as if expecting me to follow, then stomped off. I heard the scrunch of his tyres on the gravel outside, then silence fell, more welcome and refreshing than ever.

I have no idea how long I spent on that hillock. Nobody else came, and time seemed to crawl to a stop. Two bright-blue butterflies appeared and did a dance of spring courtship – or was it battle? A pair of egrets flapped back to the nest they were building in a Chinese fir just outside the enclosure. From the distance, the vagaries of air currents sent the buzz of a tractor ebbing and flowing in and out of earshot. As I lay motionless, I felt all the tension inside me fading away like ripples – the tensions of the day, then of the week, of Yanzhou and Nanjing. Then of my whole journey. Then . . .

'We're closing.' The curator was standing at the foot of the hill, with an amused smile on his face. I got up and reluctantly wished his pyramid goodbye. He and I walked slowly down the twin colonnade of yews to the gateway. In my imagination we were both feeling the same gratitude and reverence for this beautiful place.

'Do you want a beer?' he said as we reached the entrance. 'I've got some in my office. One yuan fifty.'

Disillusioned but thirsty, I accepted. As I drank the hot, sweet liquid, I watched him put his things away: his cash box, his ticket stubs, his novel, his chess set.

His chess set? I couldn't resist.

'D'you know the rules?' he replied.

'Of course.'

'Chinese, not Western.'

'Of course.'

'Okay then. You be red,' he added, once he had set up the pieces. This was *xiangqi* etiquette. Black starts and usually wins, so the host compliments the guest by assuming that the guest is the better player, and thus not in need of this advantage. Or was he just being devious?

Gun to centre three. Damn . . .

I was soon in difficulty. After a few minutes, an old man walked up to watch, took one look at the board and volunteered to act as my assistant. A few more minutes, and I had become a spectator, while the two peasants slapped their counters down on the table in quick textbook moves. I felt humbled by their expertise, and did my best to follow the tactics: the curator was building up strength in the centre; the old man attacking down the left file. But the clacking of the chessmen and the rich May heat lulled me into drowsiness, and my attention began to wander away from the game, past the village and out into the fields. A man was sitting against the bole of a poplar, beside a crate of orange squash. A tractor – the one I had heard from the temple? – came chugging past him with a load of manure; the man held out a bottle but the three young drivers (one on the seat, one on each mudguard) all shook their heads. The vendor just shrugged.

I felt high on the beauty of this scene: the patchwork fields; the line of young trees vanishing towards the Qufu road; the highway itself, reduced to silence but still trying to get in touch by heliograph . . . Just like Lingyan Shan, I said to myself, and was at once swept up in the expectation of another wave of happiness. None came, and I was filled with disappointment. Then a third feeling trumped them both – acceptance. You are here. Enjoy the experience.

I looked out at Shandong again, expecting nothing, wanting nothing. And my thoughts took wing in an even stranger way than on the mountainside. It was as if my mind had suddenly floated free of my body and was hovering weightless and formless over the landscape. In this state, I discovered, it could dart down on to any activity and become a part of it: driving a tractor, selling drinks, playing chess. I could almost feel the spirit of the land itself – timeless, nutritive, holy. I was a part of this place. I was –

But what was this 'I'?

A memory came back; that Westerner sitting on a train rattling across Guangdong province, pondering an ancient Zen riddle. The answers he had given were trite and easy. Now there was a new answer, crazy but compelling: in essence, this 'I' was nothing. Floating, protean, it had no substance, no separateness, no identity, no nature . . .

Fear of annihilation flooded into me, like the terror that must have filled Marie-Claude's father on his deathbed. Please let me be my old self again! Landbound and limited, I don't mind – I just want to be secure. But then, a moment behind it, came reassurance: 'I' was aware and alive, experiencing more acutely and passionately than ever. 'Nothing', 'something' – these were just words. Marie-Claude's riddle tore a hole in the web of logic and language, and broke free. To what? I had no idea – the feeling of freedom vanished, just as on that mountain, the moment I contemplated it.

The owner of the Confucius bicycle-hire company had done good business today: renting all his bikes out at double rates; changing Brett's hundred yuan FEC deposit into a hundred yuan *renminbi*. He invited me to join him in a bowl of beer while he finished adding up his takings.

'D'you know anything about Zen?' I asked.

He laughed. 'No. People normally ask me about Confucius. I don't know much about him, either, except that he was a very wise man.'

When the last fen was accounted for, he shut up shop, offered me a discount for a week's hire and rode off on a moped. I walked back to the hotel, past the bus station and up Queli Jie. The street was its old, quiet self again, with only echoes of the day's bustle remaining in the heat radiating from the cobbles, in the clanks and crashes of the last vendors packing their stalls away.

'Hello!' shouted the man with the headless Sage (now in three bits). How many people had become philosophers today? I wondered.

Back at the hotel Brett informed me that I had missed dinner, so I wandered down to the Drum Tower, where I bought some noodles off a stall and ate them staring up at the silhouette of the old gateway. A sense of mystery swept over me. What had that strange experience by the temple gates meant? To make a journey seemed to mean to subject oneself to a perpetual bombardment of questions that went deeper and deeper, like crashing through the floors of a cardboard house. Where would it end? At a point of knowledge? In limbo and confusion?

Just keep on exploring, I told myself. Answers will come when you're ready.

8

A Day in the Country

I gave a ting on my bell and accelerated down the straight, shimmering road out of town. We were in open country almost at once – wheat land as flat as the environs of Suzhou, but devoid of detail apart from a few whitewashed barns and the twin lines of poplars vanishing into the distance ahead of us.

'Welcome to the real China!' said Jeff. 'The countryside. Ten million square kilometers of it. Home to eight hundred million people.' The young American language teacher pedalled up beside me and grinned.

'Eight hundred million,' I said to myself. I began counting. One, two, three . . .

We left at first light, with no plan other than to ride as far as we could until we vanished off our 'Tourist Map of Qufu and District' – an aim we soon achieved. The sun began to climb up the sky, the horizon to blister into a heat haze; the sound of water tinkling along the roadside irrigation channels became irritating, then nagging, then torture . . .

'Hello!' shouted a ragamuffin boy as we coasted through his tumbledown village. We jangled our bells in reply, sending a pair of stiff-legged, self-important roosters scuttling for safety into an alley. We bumped across the rice left out on the concrete road-way for the traffic to thresh. We pedalled past a group of men pulling carts piled high with enormous Ali Baba terracotta pots.

The further we went, the poorer and tattier our surround-ings became – more mildewed thatch roofs, more potholes, less motor transport. Buses and lorries still thundered past, announcing themselves with klaxons and leaving a calling card of dust and fumes, but they no more belonged here than we did. Only two pieces of modernity had taken root on this road: one was the 'iron cow', a kind of engine on wheels, which drivers in ear-defenders hitched up to trailers and drove at a fast walking pace, deafening anyone they passed. The other was the bicycle.

In Shandong, a bike wasn't just a way of getting from one place to another. It was a family saloon, a pick-up truck, a delivery van. Each creaking, overloaded machine was a tribute to human ingenuity – the man with his family on home-made dickey seats; the basket vendor with wickerwork mushrooming from every possible attachment point. Overloaded panniers bulged with corn cobs, dripped lime, peeped with the voices of a hundred duck chicks; items rattled against the frames to which they had been lashed – spades, lengths of tubing, rusty wire. Objects had to be moved, and these practical, determined people would move them.

'Hello!' I felt honoured by the cheerful welcome we received: two idlers with no deeper motive than curiosity, with no encumbrances apart from a day pack and two water bottles.

We finally capitulated to thirst and stopped at a tiny roadside stall, where we sat in the shade of a locust tree, drinking orange squash through soggy straws and watching the traffic. The stall owner's Bakelite radio serenaded us in the background.

Hong Kong disco, a love song by Teresa Teng, then an English folk tune, arranged for piano and baritone. Britten? Vaughan Williams? It seemed the most bizarre thing in the world – but as the melody continued, its plangent, lost-world beauty overwhelmed me with its appositeness. I turned away so no one could see the tear running down my cheek . . .

'Hello!'

A group of men in baggy Mao suits and work boots was standing by a wall, watching us. One of them – the only one with pens in his breast pocket – had plucked up the courage to approach.

'*Ni hao,*' said Jeff.

The man giggled nervously. 'You speak Chinese!'

'Of course,' said my companion. (He did, excellently, even

to the extent of understanding the thick Shandong accent, and possibly even a few words of the local dialect. In the face of his skill, my growing confidence in my own Mandarin began to wilt; only when I was alone again did I recover the nerve to initiate conversations.)

'My name is Kong,' the man began. 'Kong Debao. Manager, Chongxi Number One Waste-Metal Recycling Factory.' He pointed to a long, low corrugated-iron roof behind the wall, with a grimy chimney protruding from the far end. 'Please, I would like you to meet my colleagues.'

On Kong's orders, the men stepped forward, holding out dirty, work-wrinkled hands, grinning bashful, childlike smiles.

'This is Mr Kong, our chief foreman. Our furnaceman, Mr Kong. Assistant furnaceman Kong . . .'

'All descendants of Confucius,' I said, showing off my local knowledge.

'Oh, no,' Debao replied. 'People used to change their names in the old days, to gain status. Status among outsiders, anyway,' he added snootily. 'Everyone in Shandong knew who the real Kongs were.'

'Are you one?' I asked.

'Of course! My great grandfather was the son of the seventy-third duke.'

He sent a subordinate off to make us some tea, and we talked more about his factory, economic reform and metallurgy – though conversation had a habit of creeping back to the illustrious ancestor.

'Confucius was a Communist, really. "With education, there are no class distinctions," that's what he said. Self-improvement through study,' he added, tapping those pens proudly.

'Supposing some people improve themselves more than others?' Jeff put in.

'Then society as a whole benefits.'

'But if they make more money as a result?'

'They contribute more – why shouldn't they?'

'I thought everyone was supposed to be equal,' the American continued.

'That's "ultra-leftism",' said Debao. 'Confucius never said anything about equality, anyway. Ah! Here comes the tea!'

Dr Ye had been right: political discussion was not the best way to build bridges. Exchanging gifts did the job much better: the tea was delicious, and a packet of duty-free cigarettes was received in return with a smile. When we had finished we left with friendly handshakes all round.

'We're so pleased that you want to come to China,' said Debao.

'I wish it was as easy for us to visit your country,' someone else commented.

Debao scowled. 'Reserves of foreign currency are an essential national asset . . .'

The hills began as a line of grey rising out of the haze to our left. Then the road swung towards them and soon they were less than a mile away, arid, precipitous and irresistible. We jolted off the banked highway and down on to a dirt track, plunging into silence almost at once. No more motor horns, just the creaking of our bikes and the jangle of water in sluices. And, somewhere up in that cobalt sky, a lark singing.

We reached the foot of the escarpment alone and unseen, laid the bicycles on the ground and rested, feasting on the sun and the peace. A lone carter came creaking into view with a load of stone chippings. He glanced at us and we watched him puff by. Nobody spoke – it was as if a treaty of mutual respect and noninterference had been signed.

Fifty yards on, he stopped, propped himself against the wheel of his vehicle and began staring. Then he shouted at us, in a jerky, animated voice.

'What's he saying?' I asked, nervous for the first time on this ride.

'Are we thirsty, and do we want a drink?' Jeff replied.

The carter lived in a corrugated-iron hut just out of view behind a spine of rock. There was only one room, with a wooden bed against the wall, a rusty iron stove in one corner and an enamel washstand in the other. A wooden chest of drawers stood by the door; on it was a tiny shrine with yew leaves, a candle and a creased brown photograph of a woman with tiny, bound feet and a man in a pillbox hat.

Mr Li, our host was called. He poured us cold tea from a

kettle, and we sat on the bed drinking out of brown, stained glasses. He was eager to talk – fortunately in Mandarin.

'My parents,' he said, nodding vigorously when asked about the photo. 'Just after their wedding. We used to own land here – not much, but enough to survive from, and enough for a small luxury, like a trip to Jinan, to a photographer.'

'What happened in 1949?' asked Jeff.

'Nothing much. It was only later that land was taken and made over to the commune. But I'd always supported the Communists, because they fought the Japanese. I was happy to do what they said. It was later that things went wrong. One day, our cadres got orders from Beijing to build furnaces for iron. "Iron?" we said. "There's no iron round here." But we obeyed – perhaps there was going to be another war. We stripped the hills of trees. Low-grade ore from the north came down in trucks, and we smelted it into iron that nobody could use. Meanwhile, of course, we neglected our fields. The crops failed; people went hungry; people died, especially the old and the young. It was terrible. "Just like the old days," we said.'

That was the Great Leap Forward of 1959–62. The Cultural Revolution, on the other hand, had had little effect; Li talked about it almost casually.

'Qufu was a great target for Red Guards. The people hid all the treasures, and the buggers went away empty-handed. Here? Nothing much. We pretended to listen to all these speeches, then got on with our work. We had groups of city boys and girls here, of course. They couldn't sow, plant, harvest, plough, dig, mend – anything. And their morals were low.' He looked stern for a moment, then smiled. 'Still, they were young. I was married when I was fourteen. Some of them were in their twenties and still single.' He shrugged, as if 'city boys and girls' were such bizarre creatures that normality could not be expected of them.

'And what about the present?' asked Jeff. 'Are you well off?'

Li nodded. 'My brother and I bought our old land back three years ago. We've put a lot of work into it. We grow maize, and I take the cobs into Zouxian to sell. Just as I did when I was a boy.'

'And you're happy with that?'

'Of course,' he replied, surprised we should need to ask.

I sipped my tea and looked round at the bare shack where this leathery old man was so happy; I felt very humble.

We sat at the top of the climb, exhausted but satisfied.

'Don't drink all your water at once,' Jeff warned. 'We've got a lot of cycling ahead of us.'

But nothing, surely, as tiring as lugging our machines up a mountain path on our backs. The reward was access to another Shandong: harsh and ungenerous, like Hunan or Jiangxi. In a coombe below us, a man was steering an ox-plough across a field of tinder-dry ash. Was he really planning to grow something in that? To our left, three young boys were herding a flock of mangy goats through the sparse, Sicilian thorn trees. Their clothes were ragged, their faces lined like old men's. As they passed us, they said nothing.

Happily, these mean-spirited hills were narrow – an arrow-head of bitterness jabbed into the vast fecundity of the plains. We were soon wheeling our bikes downwards again, past a set of quarries where half-naked men were hammering at boulders with wooden mallets. Just before the land levelled out, we passed a shed with a smokestack belching white dust. A group of labourers, their hands and faces caked deathly white, emerged to stare at us.

'Hello!' someone shouted, and we stopped. A thin, buck-toothed man selected himself as the spokesman.

'You are from America?'

After answering the usual questions, we asked what the men did.

'We make cement,' the man replied, flicking lime off his cheek. 'For roads, new buildings . . . Have you been to Jinan? Some of our cement has been used there. Cigarette?'

'It's too hot,' I replied, and the men laughed.

'Come here in midsummer if you want to feel too hot! This is warm. Of course, I guess you have air-conditioning in England and America – in your houses, in your cars. Do you have a car?'

'Yes. An old one, mind you . . .'

Once there, conversation remained in the groove of consumer

goods. I had to reel off a list of posessions. Yes, I had a tele-
phone, too. All to myself. And a hi-fi, and a video recorder. My
audience nodded politely, but what were they feeling? Bloated
capitalist?

I asked them. 'Do you mind the fact that we have these
things?'

They shook their heads.

'What difference does it make to us?' said the man. 'The West
is rich. One day China will be rich, too. Do you have a video
camera?'

'No,' I replied – with relief, though they looked disappointed.

Beyond the factory, we were back on the plain again, alone with
the intensity of the heat and the silence. The sun was at its height
now, trying to scorch us off the mud roads; the Chinese were
taking their *xiuxi* – how dare we defy the rules? But we did,
pedalling mechanically along a dirt track that seemed to shun all
villages, preferring instead to unroll itself in a perpetual straight
line. Features of landscape climbed head first out of the haze –
a line of poplars, an aqueduct, a finger of rock – growing to
life size, then floating past us. Only roads were absent from
the scene. It seemed we could ride on for ever and still have
only one way to go: forward.

It came to me in a flash, an understanding of what those
absurd, astronomical figures meant – ten million square kilometres, eight hundred million people. It meant this road – a
road we could ride for the rest of our lives and still not have
finished. It meant eight hundred million encounters like the
ones we had had – eight hundred million human beings as
different as Zhuang Boling, Kong Debao, Li and the man with
the buck teeth. Racists and class warriors might try to squeeze
those millions into stereotyped categories, but in reality, China
was alive with difference, with a billion life histories, births and
discoveries of the world, a billion minds, values and souls . . .

'Let's make a left,' said Jeff, pointing to a tiny, winding path.

'What – along that?'

'We'll never get back to Qufu otherwise.'

'No, I guess not.'

If each life contained a million moments . . .

We reached a town in late afternoon, having travelled the last few miles along a metalled road that made us pray for macadam for the rest of the way. On the outskirts, we found a huge brick building with crates of soft drinks visible inside the door. We parked our bikes and staggered in; coolness hit us with the force of a punch. As we wandered round the tidy, well-stocked shelves – this general store had everything, from tinned brawn to television sets – it came back to us what it felt like to have skin and shape. The manager stood behind his counter watching with amusement.

'You are thirsty?' he asked. 'We have orange, lemon, China-Cola.'

'China-Cola?'

He held up a familiar fluted bottle and pointed to its trademark in familiar round writing. 'Made in Qingdao. It's forty-seven fen. Orange is thirty-eight fen, lemon thirty-two.'

We sat gratefully down on the shop steps, while the man brought us two colas.

'You have come far?' he asked.

'From Qufu.'

'That's a journey!'

Yes . . . A young man in goggles and a face mask thundered past on a motorbike, kicking up a cloud of dust and scattering the chickens that had been loitering around the shop entrance. Oh, for something like that to get home on! The dust settled; the birds returned to their strutting and bickering. Our heavy black cycles were waiting patiently where we had left them.

'Of course, you can't go back to Qufu tonight,' the man continued. 'It'll be dark in a couple of hours. You'll get lost. And it's dangerous: nobody uses lights.' He pointed to a dust-covered box of batteries to prove his point.

'We'll have to try,' I replied half-heartedly. If we got too tired, we'd sleep under the stars – which sounded romantic, but would probably be damp, uncomfortable and insect-plagued. And was certainly illegal. (And maybe dragons emerged, when the tractors and the commissars were asleep . . .)

'There's a back room here you can use,' the man said. 'Ten yuan FEC. And you must join my family for dinner – as guests.'

We ate rice from a steel tureen and drank beer from plastic bowls, watched with pride by the Fang family: the shop manager, his wife, his father, his brother and sister-in-law, and two round-faced, staring children. Jeff dazzled them with his Mandarin, with his tales of America, with his description of somewhere almost as remote – Beijing (where he worked teaching English). Fang could only nod and say he had been to Jinan a few times.

'But we have a TV,' he added. 'Our own, private one. Through that, we see the world. Even here in Tangqiao.'

It was on in the background as we ate: *Comrade Liu*, an adventure based on the life of Liu Shaoqi, then a Shanghai opera. Then news – with an item about drug abuse in Britain.

'That's Piccadilly Circus!' I exclaimed. 'I work near there.'

Fang grinned, as pleased at the irony of the situation as I was. 'The world is small,' he commented. 'That's what Confucius said when he climbed Mount Taishan.'

'He would,' I muttered.

When darkness fell, our host walked with us back to the shop, letting us into the storeroom and spreading out blankets for us. I lay down and waited for sleep. It wouldn't come, so I went and sat on those steps. From the direction of the town, I could see the flickering screen of an open-air communal TV, its eerie, cadaverous light bouncing off the faces of the hundred or so eager watchers. Maybe Confucius had been right . . .

But in the other direction was the plain from which we had emerged. In the moonlight, it shone like water, glassy and undulating. Its rustling was like waves beating on the edge of the town. My Sea of Tranquillity, as vast as an ocean.

9

Beijing Express

'I can't wait to get to Beijing,' said Brett.

'No . . .'

'Jam, proper film, chocolate! The Friendship Store's supposed to be the best in China.'

'Yes . . .'

Friendship Stores, where overpriced souvenirs are sold exclusively to foreigners by surly assistants – how ironic that term seemed. And poignant, now that I was leaving Shandong. This was my last day in Qufu, and I was determined to make the most of it.

'You must visit the Confucius forest,' said Beth, an American academic, here for a conference on the Sage 'in the light of Marxism' and breakfasting with us to get away from the other delegates. 'It's really special. I'll come with you,' she added. 'Show you around.'

We hired a cycle-rickshaw and headed north out of the town, back into those joyfully familiar wheat fields. The sound of the wind and the play of sunlight on the waving stalks brought memories flooding back. I tried to describe our ride to her; she tried to tell me about the wisdom in the *Analects*. Our enthusiasms whizzed past each other at right angles, making no contact.

'This is a forest?'

The driver put us down beneath a massive brick wall that

ran off in either direction as if intending to encompass a town. A gateway, now guarded by a detachment of ticket vendors, admitted us to the sacred site.

'No,' said Beth as we walked in. 'It's a place of pilgrimage.'

I thought of Marie-Claude. There was nothing here that would have inspired her, just dull bumps of earth, bored-looking tourists and melancholy, drooping fir trees.

'This way.' Beth pointed down an ill-maintained cobble pathway lined with statues of soldiers and scholars. At the far end was a grass-covered mound surrounded by a breached wall.

'The Sage's tomb. Beautiful, isn't it? Simple and noble. Just the kind of memorial he'd have wanted.'

'Yes, I suppose so.' But I couldn't hold out any longer. 'Actually, I don't know enough about Confucius to comment. What I have read about him, I don't like. All that stuff about ritual . . .'

Beth looked bitterly upset. 'Oh. I thought you'd have a better understanding. You seem to like China. You can't do that and despise Confucius, you know. He made this country what it is.'

'Today? Still?' Ater the Long March, after forty years of Communism and Western technology?

'Of course.'

We walked past a cluster of steles – stone tablets inscribed with Sagely wisdom, now illegible with age and neglect. What was it Lao Zi had said about Confucianism?

> When the Way is lost, there are virtues,
> When virtues are lost, there are good intentions,
> When good intentions are lost, there are rules,
> And when rules are lost, there are rites.

'Tell me about him, then,' I said. 'Change my views.'

'I can't,' she replied. 'Only you can do that. Go home and read. Not just the *I Ching* and the *Daodejing*, the way most travellers do, but the *Analects* and the *Book of Songs*. You'll meet a very remarkable man, humane, gentle, idealistic; a man who loved life. *Ren* – humanity – that was his absolute value. Not obedience or formality.'

'So why this obsession with ritual?'

Beth shook her head. 'Because people need structure and discipline in their lives. Confucius made a distinction between the form and the spirit of the rites – between what he called *li* and *yi*. The first led the individual to the second, which was what really mattered.'

'Which was . . .?'

'Respect – for others, for oneself, for the roles people have to play in society, and the essential humanity underneath those roles.'

We walked a few more paces.

'Supposing people don't accept the roles?'

'Then you get anarchy. As happened in his lifetime. And the lifetime of these people.' She pointed to a group of Chinese visitors. 'In America, we're rediscovering the true nature of violence. In China they know it already. That's why there is respect for the old sages again.' She sighed. 'And that's why this conference is a waste of time – not just when Party hacks from Beijing get up to speak, but from beginning to end, in its whole conception. Marxism is a philosophy of violence; Confucianism of peace. Marxism calls itself humanistic, but in reality it just deals in impersonal social forces. What has it got to say about the moral development of the individual? Nothing. For Confucius, that was the key. He understood what Marx never realized, that the only way to have a decent society is to have decent people in charge of it.'

I thought of Nanjing, and nodded. Beth pointed up at the statues we were passing: their limbs and faces had been hacked off.

'That's what happens if you don't,' she continued.

Yes – but how did she propose that these 'decent' people should gain and retain power? Especially when confronted with opponents who did this sort of thing to human beings, let alone to statues. Looking up at the sheer, split heads of the Sage's guardians, I wondered for a moment if another Chinese philosopher hadn't been wiser than Confucius or Marx – the 'legalist' Han Fei, who argued that men were evil and could only be compelled to behave decently by an absolute ruler who enforced laws with uncompromising severity. The tyrant

Qin Shihuang had followed Han's teachings to the letter, and had made China into a nation, banishing its enemies behind a Great Wall, building up trade, literacy and wealth.

We reached the mound and stood in silence, Beth lowering her head in religious awe. I stood beside her, trying to feel the same emotion, and failing. I heard a shuffling sound behind me and turned round. An old woman was hobbling painfully towards us on two bamboo walking sticks. Her feet were tiny and arched, like hooves: in girlhood they would have been bound, to make them grow into this unnatural shape. More criticisms of the Sage flooded into my mind. If he had really 'made this country what it is', wasn't he responsible for cruelties like this?

'Footbinding was a Tang-dynasty innovation,' said Beth, before I could open my mouth. 'Confucius would never have approved.'

'How can you say that?'

'He taught responsibility, not servitude or exploitation. Five relationships: ruler, subject; father, son; husband, wife; the relationship between younger and older siblings; and that between younger and older friends. All of them were reciprocal, none of them just one-way. All of them involved duties and obligations. They linked the weak and the strong together, not like the all-against-all we have in the West, or the class hatred they keep stirring up here. Western men fall a long way short of his standards,' she added, with a deep, private bitterness that made me unwilling to pursue the matter any further.

The old lady bowed before the tomb, the anguish gone from her face. I still wanted to shake her by the shoulders and lecture her about freedom and rights, about Sartre's notion of *mauvaise foi* and how oppressors cheat people into loving them. But instead I just stared, at her pious, contented eyes and praying lips. Like the old man in Lingyan Shan, she radiated a faith and a serenity that I could only envy.

'Of course, China has often fallen short, as well,' Beth said after a pause. 'But at least the ideals were there.'

But everyone had ideals: Confucius, Han Fei, Mao . . . Trouble was, they were all different. What mankind needed was truth, truth about what we are and how we should live. It suddenly seemed an unattainable goal.

As we turned to go, my companion gave another gentle bow towards Confucius' tomb. I followed her example, out of shame, politeness and, above all, confusion.

I walked quickly through the village, wondering if I had left myself enough time. Supposing it shut early? I reached the fields. Not far now. There it was – that walled enclosure I had seen on my first day here. And now it was open.

I increased my pace still further. A few hundred yards short of the gates, I heard the noise of an engine, and a minibus came bumping past me. It pulled up exactly where I was headed and deposited a batch of queasy-looking group-tourists.

'Damn!' After the tomb of Shao Hao, I didn't want to share this place with anyone else. So I slowed down to a stroll; when I reached the entrance I loitered outside, smiling at an old man with a wispy white Confucius beard and trying to talk with him.

'What's the temple called? Is it very old? What's it for?'

Were his replies in dialect, or Mandarin? Either way, I didn't understand a word he said – except when the tour group reappeared; then he produced a clay pipe and shouted in English: 'Take picture! One yuan!' The bus jolted off into the distance, leaving me alone with my ignorance. A familiar feeling . . .

A straight, yew-lined 'spirit path' led up through a series of courtyards. This is the standard layout of Chinese temples, which has been compared to a flight of spiritual locks, raising temple-goers from the worldliness outside to the devoutness with which they should enter the great hall at the far end. These locks, however, seemed to have sprung a leak. The first ones were full of chipped steles and unkempt grass, and the second included a foul-smelling open lavatory. On a terrace in the last one stood the hall, its eaves pallid with age, its roof tiles dull and cracked. A vendor lurked by the entrance, selling joss sticks and soft drinks.

'You like?' she asked as I climbed the final steps. I shook my head and went in – the climactic moment of worship for the believer, an act of routine banality for the tourist.

The hall was dank and gloomy, smelling of mildew and stale

incense. Peeling paint hung from its beams; the floor was splintery and uneven. And it was bare – just a wooden box for an altar, with a simple painted statue of a stocky, round-faced man in a blue robe and a bizarre mortarboard hat, gazing out through the door with surprised boggle-eyes. Who was he? He was sitting bolt upright, like a nervous subordinate in the presence of a tyrannical superior – he wasn't a great emperor, that was certain. His heavy, booted feet were planted squarely in front of him, his hands crossed defensively over his chest – he was no philosopher, either. Confucius would have run rings round him, unless they were arguing about the price of a pig. It looked as if an old Shandong man had walked into this room, tried on some robes he found lying on the floor, climbed up on the dais – and had been turned to painted wood.

'You like?' The vendor's voice broke into my thoughts.

'No,' I snapped angrily.

'Bring good luck.'

'I don't –'

'Good luck – yes?'

'No!'

'Yes?'

'Oh, for heaven's sake . . . All right.'

She grinned. 'Two bundle?'

'One's fine.'

'Two better.'

'I only want one. Understand?'

'Yes.' She walked over to an urn and placed two sets of sticks in it.

'Who is this?' I asked resignedly, pointing up at the man.

'King Wu,' she replied as she lit the fat brown tapers. 'Founder of Zhou dynasty.'

'Ah. Of course!'

Confucius had lived in the 'Spring and Autumn' period, a time of continuous strife between various Chinese princedoms. The Zhou dynasty had ended two hundred years before; it had been a time of unity, order and prosperity (until its last days, when it became decadent). Confucius had looked back at the early and middle years of the Zhou as a golden age, an age whose spirit China would have to recover before it could enjoy civilization again. This simple figure represented his ideal ruler, firm but benevolent; the people's father, their older brother and guiding friend.

Smoke began swirling round the old king and up into the beamwork. I took a deep breath and let the sweet, heavy smell of sandalwood fill my lungs. An image came into my mind of priests in brocade robes, of gongs and chanting, melodies on bamboo flutes and a silk-stringed *erhu*. I imagined peasants at prayer at a time of crisis, looking up at this figure in trust and hope. China seemed stranger than ever, yet closer: the world still needed such rulers. Then the age of this still-pertinent symbol struck me with its full force. Three thousand years. This man had ruled when the pharaohs were founding Thebes, when Athens and Sparta were peasant villages – in 1027 BC, five centuries before the Celts came to Britain (but when the Middle Kingdom already had a millennium of history). In that instant I had understanding of China's vastness in time, to go with that endless Shandong dirt track, which told me of its vastness in space and humanity.

An endless track . . . Hegel had once said that China had no history – a remark usually quoted to show the great German philosopher's blinkered Eurocentrism. But he had been right, if history meant civilizations that burgeoned and decayed, leaving nothing but fragments. In China dynasties rose and fell, but beneath these surface disturbances there flowed a great, uninterrupted river, deeper and wider with each cycle – Shang, Zhou, Qin, Han . . . We walk round the Parthenon or Pompeii – or down Whitehall – and ponder the transitoriness of empire; the Chinese bow at the tomb of Confucius or light joss sticks beneath King Wu, and gaze down an unbroken 'spirit path' into their deepest past. And a light bounces straight back, illuminating their immediate present.

Another thought struck me, strangest of all. (A dam of ignorance was bursting in this bizarre, tatty hall.) This great river of Chinese life had risen and grown in almost complete isolation from Europe. A few traders had come from Rome; a few medieval adventurers had marvelled and returned home; hordes of missionaries and imperialists had barged in uninvited and been sent packing, baffled and dissatisfied. But now, for the first time in all those millennia, China was opening itself voluntarily to the West. And not just to 'experts', but to ordinary people; to me, Don and Marie-Claude, to anyone curious or restless enough to come. 'Plunge into our river!' it was saying. 'Immerse yourselves in it. Test your views and experiences against our four thousand years.'

The privilege was overpowering. Me, with my beginner's Mandarin and my college-kid ideas about Confucius: how the hell did I deserve it? There could only be one answer: I didn't. But I was here anyway – despite my ignorance, despite my arrogance. I had a duty to be grateful, to be humble, to relish my fortune, to enrich my soul with the most honest emotion a traveller can feel: wonder.

I stood for a long time, staring up at King Wu and slowly filling with a new lightness of spirit, the way a room gradually but inevitably fills with smouldering incense. China's age and immensity would always outstretch my understanding; my 'conclusions' about it would always be starting points – provisional, good-as-possible guesses. ('All that learning to do . . .') And how silly those dismal, superior people looked, who had 'known' all about this vast, ancient country.

I gave a bow to the old king and an apology to the spirit of the Sage, then walked out into the Shandong sunshine.

Our alarms went off at four thirty. Half an hour later, three young Westerners padded out of the Confucius Mansion Hotel and down Queli Jie: Jeff, returning refreshed to his teaching; Brett, eager for modernity; me, sad to leave but (at last!) philosophical. We walked down deserted streets to the bus station, where we found a few rickshaw men sleeping in their vehicles and a cook selling noodles from a stall. A small group of peasants sat guzzling breakfast at a trestle table; we joined them and drank tea while dawn broke with tropical speed. Brett glanced at his watch.

'Is this bus coming?' he said.

A few minutes later, a motor horn sounded. A van pulled up, disgorging a complement of workmen in Mao suits and a bleary-eyed traveller, fresh from a night at the Yanzhou Hotel.

'Are you going back?' I asked the driver. He nodded. We

gulped the rest of our *cha* and scrambled on board. Once we had settled into our seats, he switched off the engine and got out.

'What's he doing?' asked Brett.

'Ordering breakfast, it looks like,' Jeff replied. 'He's probably filling in time till the bus is full.'

'Full?' Brett glanced round at the empty seats. 'We'll miss the train at that rate.'

The driver ate his noodles slowly, winding the pasta round his chopsticks as if this were a new art form, halfway between ballet and sculpture. Then he paid, sauntered back to his cab and took out a film magazine. One more passenger boarded. Six more required . . .

'Jesus,' Brett muttered. 'Another day in this bloody place . . .'

Suddenly the engine revved into life. At once the men who had been idling by the stall leapt to their feet, ran over to us and began fighting for seats. The door slammed shut behind them. Another morning's game of bluff was over. We had a train to catch.

'Beijing?' I asked. I wanted to say the word with enthusiasm, but it came out as a tired drawl. I was leaving Shao Hao, the Drum Tower, King Wu . . .

The official pointed to a large open-sided shed with rows of wooden benches. 'Wait there.'

We settled down – Jeff with a book; Brett glancing around with a pointless, childlike terror, as if some nameless evil was lurking behind the advertising hoardings for Taishan electric fans and Double Whale shirts. I began to feel sorry for the young traveller, but there was too much going on around me to spend time cheering him up. A beggar with a withered arm was making his way round the passengers, most of whom gave him a few fen. Then a second mendicant appeared, with no visible deformity. This proved too much for a man in a suit, who jumped to his feet and started shouting:

'Look, there are foreigners here! What will they think?'

Nobody took the beggars' side, and they slunk off. Traders replaced them, selling peanuts, packet noodles and comic-strip story books about the Long March, China's Vietnam war or

the legend of the Yellow Emperor. In the background, a goods
train lumbered past – two steam engines and half a mile of
the Chinese economy: cattle, tree trunks, coal, wire, bricks,
bamboo, chemicals, piping . . . The station tannoy made an
incomprehensible announcement.

'Five minute!' said the man next to me.

'Ah, you speak English.'

He grinned back, but before we could get into conversation, the official blew a whistle and began shooing us on
to the platform. A man emerged from an office and told
us to wait behind a yellow line. Silence fell, broken by the
distant lowing of a siren and the clatter of wheels. The noise
grew louder and louder until a massive diesel emerged out
of Yanzhou's early-morning mist – the Beijing Express. For
a moment, nobody moved; then, on a secret, Chinese-only
signal, the crowd broke ranks and stormed the still-moving
doors, yanking them open and barging past anyone trying to
get off.

We were among the last on board, by which time there were
no seats, and rush-hour jams had formed in the the aisles and
corridors.

'It's only six hundred kilometers,' said Jeff with a shrug. 'I've
stood for further than that. When I went to Xi'an . . .'

'I want to go home,' said Brett.

I sat back and rested my head against the antimacassar, gazing
out at the countryside and wiggling my toes in their Chinese
Railways slippers.

'More tea?' asked Mr Hu.

'Thank you.'

He lifted the lid of my porcelain Chinese Railways cup.

We were travelling 'soft seat' as guests of Hu and Peng, two
marine engineers from Shanghai, who had met us in the corridor
and insisted that we spend the rest of the journey with them.
They were on their way to finalize a joint venture with a Japanese
company, an occasion for which they had dressed in Mao suits,
creaseless and perfectly tailored, to go with their starched white
shirts and shining brogues.

Peng's English matched his appearance. 'You asked about

the Four Modernizations,' he said, with a slight American accent. 'Agriculture, industry, science, defence. China's most basic need is an efficient rural economy, to feed both itself and the cities . . .'

We passed a level crossing where two cyclists and a mule-cart stood waiting. The mule driver looked up and grinned at my Western face.

'Jobs will be lost, so industry must expand. To do this, we must become globally competitive . . .'

A man was shooing a flock of ducks along the bank of a canal.

'Resource use is so inefficient at the moment . . .'

Newly arrived in the People's Republic and expecting barrages of Mao-speak, I would have found these words homely and reassuring. Now they filled me with distaste. 'Modernization' was a whirlwind: it would roar through Shandong, sucking up people like Li the carter and depositing them miles away from their ancestral land, in soulless, 'efficient' tower blocks. Kong Debao's factory would be deemed 'inefficient' and have to close. Fang's TV would abandon Shanghai opera and ham-fisted propaganda for soap opera and slick advertising. Nowhere would be safe. A horrible vision welled up before me of a future humanity engulfed by a great flood of uniformity, vulgarity and commercialism. 'One world' – such a noble ideal, except that it would be a world reduced to its lowest common denominator, a global market for mass-produced consumer goods, where the only journeys of exploration could be to theme parks or into nightmare fantasy worlds of gadgetry or drugs. Where would our great-grandchildren – Western or Eastern – be able to go travelling to find time, space, silence, wholeness, humanity and wonder?

Hu was pointing animatedly out of the window. 'Look!' he said. 'We approach Huang He!'

The land was streaked with bars of yellow-grey sand, which grew thicker and more frequent until they swallowed the fields up altogether. Then we approached a huge embankment, through which an enormous iron sluice gate allowed us on to a girder bridge. The second river of China – and the sixth of the world – was swirling beneath us. It was gone in a moment;

we were hustled out through another giant gate, back into the desert of silt.

'Is that it?' said Brett.

'Narrow but swift!' Hu replied.

The Yellow River. Every other waterway I had seen in China had been crowded with steamers, skiffs, sampans and barges. This one was empty. It was unusable, a mass of whirlpools and eddies, clawing at its banks and churning round the piers of the bridge as if in paroxysms of rage. Once, it had had the freedom to change its course at will, from one channel to another, even to a different mouth five hundred miles to the south.

'The Sorrow of China,' said Peng.

Millions had died in Shandong, Hebei and Jiangsu every time the river had exercised that freedom. But now, thanks to modern technology, it was penned in by the huge defences we had just crossed. Such tragedies were 'history'.

I gave a long sigh. Two things I could know about the Middle Kingdom: it had no choice but to move into the contemporary world, and visitors from countries which already enjoyed the fruits of modernity had no right to complain.

It was mid-afternoon. The landscape changed slowly, from fields and communes to factories and estates of tiny detached houses, each with a TV aerial sticking out of the roof.

'Tianjin!' said Hu.

Peng began a lecture on the economic development of China's third city. We rolled past polluted canals and yards littered with rusting wire, into a station full of electric trains. Steam engines? I hadn't seen one for two hours. This busy, modern terminus probably hadn't seen one for years.

'We're making good time,' Hu added. 'We'll reach Beijing in two hours.'

Beijing ... I had felt no emotion at the mention of the capital, because the story on the travellers' grapevine was of a dull, westernized gridiron of office blocks, with a few relics preserved in it for the tourists. But now I could feel a childlike enthusiasm building up in our Chinese hosts, not just for their business deal, but for their capital: theirs and a billion of their compatriots'. Even if there was nothing to see in Beijing, I ought to be eager to experience it. And in reality, look what there was: Tiananmen Square, the Forbidden City, the Temple of Heaven . . . I ought to be thrilled!

And suddenly I was.

10

The Dragon Takes Flight

The train traced a long, slow arc through the southern suburbs, allowing us two tantalizing views of Qianmen and the Temple of Heaven on fire with evening light before pulling into the grey metal barrel of Beijing main station.

'Welcome to the capital of the People's Republic,' said Peng. Our urbane, businesslike hosts suddenly looked edgy and overawed.

'We've really appreciated your company,' I replied, trying to give them a boost. 'Good luck in your negotiations.'

'Yeah, give 'em hell,' Jeff added.

Peng smiled. That wasn't how one did business in China – on the surface, at least.

Then they were gone. I resisted the temptation to sneak a pair of Chinese Railways slippers into my bag, and we padded out into the carpeted corridor. My feet sank into the pile one last time. The 'real China' was waiting for us on the platform: globules of spittle on the hard, slippery concrete; ruthless pushing and shoving round the exit; loudspeakers quacking and screaming. Stations are a traveller's nemesis: you've had your motion, your pretty landscape and your brief encounters; now you're one of the crowd again, as mobile as your blistered feet, as secure as your hopes of finding accommodation.

Jeff led us through the main concourse – a temple in traditional style to the modern god of mobility – and out on to a crowded concrete plaza.

'That's where you want to go,' he said, pointing through the human maze. 'Bus 106. You'll find it. *Zaijian*!'

'*Zaijian*!' And the American was gone, heading for his college in the north of the city.

'What does *zai-jian* mean?' asked Brett.

So this was the capital. It was certainly different from Shandong. Women wore make-up, slacks and blouses; men bush jackets, Terylene flares and coloured shirts. Hawkers were out in force, selling maps, changing money, recommending hotels.

'You want hashish?' one whispered.

But the old China was here as well: peasants huddled behind stockades of luggage, besieged cowboys staring out at encircling Indians as the Beijingers flowed all round them. Many belonged to minority peoples – Miao, Bai, Dai, Uygur – their raffish, colourful clothes setting off their dark, puzzled faces. This was supposed to be their capital, too, but they looked as confused and out of place as I felt.

'Nice to see some other travellers,' said Brett as we entered the foyer of the Qiaoyuan Hotel.

'I guess so.'

We tagged ourselves behind a group of backpackers haggling with the clerk over a few yuan. A tall, blonde-haired woman walked past, her breasts wobbling provocatively under her clinging T-shirt. 'Asian men are disgusting,' she was complaining. 'They stare the whole time.'

Brett and I took a double room. I was tired of his company, but he looked so sorry for himself that I didn't have the heart to ask for two singles. He grabbed the key from the receptionist and scuttled upstairs; I wandered into the bar.

'Hi,' I said to the first person I met.

'Hello,' he replied.

'Having a good trip?'

'No.'

'Oh. Why not?'

'This hotel. It's the worst I've ever stayed in. It's so dirty –'

'Just like the rest of China,' his girlfriend put in. 'These people have no notion of cleanliness. They spit, they smell, their children defecate in the streets . . .'

'Yes, we're leaving as soon as possible.'

A young Chinese in trainers and a sweatshirt – clearly a *huaqiao*, from overseas – stood by the bar. I introduced myself, and he bought me a Beijing brand beer.

'I'm George,' he added, pumping my hand like a salesman. 'Come and join us – over here. This is my friend Paul.' A thin Westerner looked up resentfully from a table.

'So, how do you find China?' I began.

'Same as ever,' he replied. 'I live here.'

Paul grimaced, as if he had heard this line before.

'I'm a student. Peking University. I come here to meet people and to practise my English. Cheers!'

'Cheers!' I sat back in the hard plastic seat.

'I know I shouldn't be here,' George continued. 'This place is for Westerners only. But there's a back door into most places in China.' He laughed. 'The manager is a good friend. I have lots of friends.' (Not Paul, who was now looking at him with real hatred.)

'To friends,' I said, raising my can.

'To friends. D'you like music?'

'Yes.'

'Rock?'

'Some.'

'Beatles, Stones, Led Zeppelin?'

'Sure.'

'Have you got any cassettes? I make copies and give them to my friends. And I do mean give.'

I shook my head. 'It's a nice idea, though.' (Was it? Rock's aggression, its easy-come, easy-go intensity – here, in China? But if 'modernity' was a package deal . . .)

'I play in a band,' George went on. 'Guitar and vocals – that's me – bass, drums and keyboards. We do our own material, plus a few cover versions, of course.'

'Of?'

'Western songs. "Get Back", "Satisfaction", "Stairway to Heaven".'

'D'you give concerts?' I asked. 'Stairway to Heaven', live in Beijing . . .

George shook his head. 'Only for friends. The Ministry of Culture controls all public performances, you see, and –'

'You could always defy the Ministry of Culture,' Paul put in. 'Though you wouldn't guess it now, rock music in the West used to be against the establishment.'

George shrugged. 'I don't want trouble,' he said. 'I want a decent job when I leave college.'

Paul looked even more disgusted.

'Tell me about your own compositions,' I said hastily. 'What do you write about?'

'Same as everyone else, I guess,' George replied. 'Girls, romance, having a good time –'

'Nothing political,' said Paul. 'Mustn't offend anyone important.'

George nodded cheerfully. 'Quite right!' Had he missed the irony or was he ignoring it?

We chatted about music for a while, until the young Beijinger looked at his Swatch and said that he had to go.

'Must be home by ten,' he said. 'Bye-bye!'

'*Zaijian.*'

Paul didn't wait until George was out of earshot before exclaiming, in a loud voice: 'What a prick!'

I shrugged. 'He bought us a beer . . .'

'Bugger the beer. People like him are ruining this country with their nepotism and their greed, with their "friends" in high places and their shallow, selfish careerism.'

'He's only nineteen!'

'So? He's still a parasite, a worm eating its way into the system and bloating itself on other people's labour. Mao was right. You have to have perpetual revolution. Look what happens the moment you relax things. Capitalism comes crawling back in through that bloody "back door".'

'But the Chinese don't want perpetual revolution. I've talked to people –'

'So have I,' Paul cut in. 'Self-satisfied, middle-class gits, who think they're marvellous because they're westernized, and don't give a damn about the people who do the real work. The truth about this country is that people want what they're told to want – by characters like 'George' and his bloody top-brass family. Look at the amount of propaganda there's been since 1976.'

He looked around him, as if seeking an ally, then sighed and sank back into his seat.

'I believed in China before I came here,' he said, after a long pause. 'In the People's Republic, in the spirit of Yan'an and Dazhai. I believed there was one place on earth where people put communal interests above their own, where work was rewarded more highly than influence or playing with money. But it looks like I was wrong. And it's 'George' and his friends who are to blame – whether they're nineteen or ninety.'

Suddenly I needed to escape from this place, from its smoke and its bitterness, and to be alone with the real China – the China that had vanished the moment I became surrounded by Westerners. I made an excuse and left, hurrying out through the glass swing doors to the forecourt, where I was accosted by two money-changers and a man selling fruit from a barrow.

'Hello!' added a pedicab driver, nearly running me over.

Beyond the road to Yongdingmen was a grass-banked cutting with a canal in it. There was no boat traffic, but the poplar trees along the towpath whispered a gentle welcome. I relaxed; I stood still; I took a deep breath of fresh air to clear my lungs. It stank of sewage and petrol. I walked down to a bridge where traffic was roaring in and out of the city centre – the noise was deafening. Beyond it, an enormous arc-lit building site mushroomed up into the night. The lights reflected on the canal, to reveal a surface rainbowed with oil, broken only by a flotilla of polystyrene containers. A man was fishing by the light of a hurricane lamp on the far bank. He hadn't caught a thing.

Beijing was a boom town. The capital's population was exploding; its resources, in this Third World country with its First World pride, were limited. Its problems, new every day, were already way beyond the grasp of experience or ideology, in a realm of difficulty of which Westerners had no inkling. If we were upset by China's failure to live up to our dreams, whose fault was that?

A pillar of glorious sunlight shafted through the torn net curtains. I got up and threw open the window. Beijing began serenading me with hooters, engines, cranes and bike bells – a great, new city calling me to share in the adventure of travelling. My heart leapt in response.

'Get pissed last night?' a voice muttered.

'No.'

'Can you shut that window then?'

I breakfasted alone, then strode along the canal bank to Yongdingmen bus station.

'Tiananmen Guangchang?' a conductor shouted.

Tiananmen Square! 'Yes! Wait for me!'

Now, in 1991, that name has such bitter overtones. But in 1985, when China was just emerging from its isolation, it conjured up only excitement. I thought of Wang and his reasons for enthusing about it as a teenager. Since then even more history had been added – the Tiananmen Incident of 1976, when mass demonstrations in memory of Zhou Enlai brought down the now infamous Gang of Four. I thought of those May Day parades – extravagant displays of patriotic pride in the largest public square in the world. 'The heart of our nation' . . . (How pointed a gesture the students' occupation of it was, and no wonder it so enraged the old men of Zhongnanhai.)

Even as the bus pulled into Qianmen Dajie, the long straight approach to the base of the square, I half expected to be stopped and told I could go no further. But we drove on, crawling up the busy shopping street towards the stark, martial façade of Qianmen Gate, finally stopping under the horned monsters of Zhengyangmen, the beautiful blue-tiled pavilion behind it. Passengers poured out on to the pavement – a businessman, an army officer, a Hong Kong lady in a bright green dress – all to stand in Tiananmen Square.

A grey plain stretched out in front of me, windswept and unpopulated, apart from the small queue at Mao's mausoleum and a few knots of tourists and vendors. Round the edges ran four-lane boulevards. They were just as empty, except for one Hongqi limousine and a clutch of jangling cyclists making their way past the long, low roofs of Tiananmen (the Gate of Heavenly Peace, from which the square takes its name) along the far end. By the concrete pillar of the Martyrs' Memorial stood a line of flagpoles. They were unadorned, their halyards slapping idly in the wind, making a cold, lonely noise that filled this place and made it sound like a seaside resort in winter.

Perhaps no one dared come here. Even in 1985, the great square seemed haunted – by its creator, Mao. His portrait stared down from the old gateway, one of the last pieces of personality cult left in China. The buildings all round me – stone-faced blocks in totalitarian neo-classical style – reflected his taste and vision: mass, martial, functional. Along the top, on Chang'an Boulevard, forty-foot hoardings celebrated his mentors: Marx, Engels, Lenin and Stalin. Stalin . . . was his ghost here, too?

A knot of people had begun to congregate in the centre, and I crossed over to join them. They weren't tourists but Chinese; they scrummaged round a wizened, denim-clad man who was squatting on the flagstones, assembling a home-made kite. He worked in Zen silence, ignoring us (and Mao and Stalin) as he clipped on the tail of crimson ribbon and tugged at the sections of the jointed, angular body to check their robustness. A dragon was coming into being, here at our feet. When it was finished, the man picked it up and hooked his string to its lower jaw. Its eyes rattled impatiently, now eager to be airborne; he remained impassive, lifting his head to sense the exact strength and direction of the wind; he waited.

With one move he threw the kite forward and jerked on its string, whiplashing it into the air. It caught the current perfectly and hurtled up into the sky, setting his string-wheel whirring and dragging a long gasp of admiration from every spectator. Within a minute, the dragon was higher than all the flagpoles or the colonnades – a tiny, bobbing symbol of defiant individuality.

Maybe the spirit of this place could not tolerate such cheek. Suddenly, as if on orders from Party HQ, the wind died. The string went slack and the man began frantically winding, no longer aloof and expert, but alone, panicky and helpless. The kite hovered aloft for an instant – like a cartoon character who has run over a cliff but not yet realized the fact – then nosedived on to the concrete, where it smashed into several pieces.

'What d'you mean, sixteen rooms?' The man was bright red from the effort of crossing the huge, cobbled courtyard behind us, and now also with anger. 'There's only one room in there!'

He pointed into the Gate of Supreme Harmony with a neurotic stab of his finger.

'In Chinese architecture, "room" is used as unit of measurement,' his guide replied coolly.

'How bloody silly! I mean, 'room' – look at it. How many rooms d'*you* think are in there?' He turned to me in an attempt to drag a fellow foreigner into the argument.

'Five,' I said skittishly.

'There's one. *One!*'

I felt guilty at once. This was the gate from which Kangxi and Qianlong had surveyed the world's mightiest armies, the gate we had approached across the massive parade ground, marvelling at its delicacy and, as we got closer, at its sheer size. Now we were beside it, beneath those staggered vermilion archways and that perfect asymptote roof, looking in – at a dingy collection of moth-eaten banners, discoloured furniture and threadbare carpets.

'This bloody country,' the man continued. 'I mean, look at the stuff in there. Rubbish! Like everything else here.'

Travelling, I was learning, can do that to people.

Another courtyard followed; it was even larger, with an even finer hall at the far end: Taihedian, shimmering as if it had just landed from another planet. It, too, was filled with dust-grey knick-knacks. Was that cramped, comfortless seat really the Dragon Throne?

The guide began intoning more facts and figures; the angry man now stood expressionless at the back of the group, his rage crushed. Bored by the guide and made shameful by the man, I made my escape down a side alley and along a damp, decaying corridor into a small quadrangle, where I could be alone again. No expectations, no dilemmas – just me and China, the way it had been in Shandong.

But this wasn't Shandong. I stared round at the cobbles the colour of bleached bones and the ochre stucco cracking off the walls. Above them, on the sagging roofs, a lone sapling was trying to root itself in a gully. Shandong had been green and flourishing: here there was only this one sign of life. Everything else was dead; sterile and spooky, like the ruins of a long-abandoned civilization on the edge of a desert that was encroaching day by day, outpost by outpost.

Confucius had taught that the emperor's duty was to his subjects, like a father's to his children. But here in the Forbidden City, these words had been ignored. Two dynasties had isolated themselves behind its picture-book walls, and degenerated from soldiers and statesmen into pantomime martinets. Twice, the anger of their misruled people had blazed up into rebellious retribution – and the decay all around me was the result. It served this Forbidden City right – its halls and courtyards were a monument to power and its abuse, to history Nanjing-style.

'Only emperor, eunuchs and concubines allowed in this part of palace,' a megaphone screeched as I passed through the Gate of Heavenly Purity. I imagined the late Ming and Qing emperors in orgies of heavenly impurity with their foot-bound concubines, attended by sexless, giggling retainers in a sick festival of the perverse, vicious and unnatural – while outside, the people for whom they were responsible suffered the all too natural pains of hunger. A stone *qilin* scowled at me for such irreverence; I scowled back and headed for the exit. Ahead of me was Jingshan, the artificial hill on which the last Ming emperor Chongzhen had hung himself at the fall of his dynasty. Justice!

Today, traffic roared along a main road, and a vendor tried to overcharge me for a bottle of orange juice. It was great to be back.

I stood in the heart of the Temple of Heaven, in the circular, triple-roofed Qinian Hall, and wondered how those late Ming and Qing emperors had felt here, alone with the spirits of the ancestors they had so feebly let down. Beneath this hammerbeam cupola and its meticulously sculpted joints of turquoise, blue and vermilion, when they had come to say the prayers on which their whole nation depended, had they understood how they were betraying their inheritance? I wanted to think yes, but the reaction of their subjects' descendants told me no.

Modern Chinese treated the temple with casual disrespect, clambering all over once sacred altars, stuffing gargoyles' mouths with litter, clustering round incense burners to see whose one-fen coin would stick to the side longest. Even here in the great hall, they wandered in and out, losing interest the moment they noticed the sign saying 'No Photography'. From the smells and stains, it was obvious that people had urinated against the columns. I was in that ruined city again, in a section taken over by illiterate nomads.

The huge mound of yellow clay right next to the temple buildings stamped official approval on this attitude. Taller than the Qinian, it dated from Mao's 'Dig Tunnels Deep' campaign of the Sixties, when Beijingers had dug into the earth of their city with trowels to hollow out a network of nuclear shelters. Useless, of course – the tunnels weren't deep enough, and the occupants would have fried had a real atom bomb been dropped. Their only effects had been to lower the city's water table, drying up many important wells and springs, and to create tons of hand-scooped subsoil with nowhere to go. Some had ended up here, in Tiantan Park, as a deliberate insult to the feudal past. Now the mound was an embarrassment, especially to the Tourism Department. A few shrubs apart, nothing would grow on it, and it was unremittingly, incurably ugly. The only way to avoid looking at it was to climb it.

At least there'll be a view, I told myself. And there was: the crouching blue-tiled temples; the office blocks springing up like weeds round the park boundaries; the Forbidden City, beyond them, half lost in smog. Nice, but not what I had come here for.

Suddenly I was furious. Anger was boiling up inside me at these tawdry, wasted monuments; at the city which surrounded them; at the civilization of which they were supposed to be the holiest shrines. And most of all at myself, for doing what I knew was wrong – blaming Beijing for not being what I wanted it to be. Just what those stupid people at the Qiaoyuan had done. But I couldn't help it. I had arrived with such expectations, stoked up by moments of incomprehensible beauty in quiet, intensely Chinese places like Suzhou and Qufu. I was in the capital: this should be the climax of my journey and there should be more moments of even greater strangeness and beauty. I wanted those marvellous traveller's highs, and I wanted them bigger and better, here and now!

Disgust replaced anger: I was reacting like an addict deprived of his fix. And, in doing so, I was making the ultimate insult to all that I had felt, seen and done on my journey – treating those glorious moments as nothing but a new form of drug.

But was that all they were?

A 'travel junkie', I had called Marie-Claude – then been overcome with guilt. But maybe those immediate intuitions had been right. Maybe that was all travelling was – a smarter, cleverer, more elite form of self-indulgence than good old home-town consumerism, but just as empty, just as dishonest. And all that talk of growth and spirituality, of questions, waiting and readiness – maybe that was all just a part of the lie. I felt that history had been dismissed as the puppeteer – to be replaced by a stupid, selfish, spoilt child, enslaved to an endless stream of meaningless, clamouring wants.

I took a lump of mud and hurled it at the temple in frustration; it landed halfway down the hill and broke into tiny pieces. I sank to my haunches and sat, head in hands.

'Travelling's an art,' I heard Don say.

So is self-deception.

'Let China come to you,' he added.

Pop philosophy! I'd root out every lie I had heard since leaving England, if it cost me every happy memory!

'I fancy a bowl of the local beer.' His voice again.

At least this time, he was talking sense.

Next day, I hired a bike and rode off aimlessly into the capital's back streets. Smelly, uneven and narrow, they led me to the banks of the Tonghui River, where I found a town of planks, plastic and sacking – shanties, the worst I had seen in China. Women in dirty clothes sat nursing quiet, underfed children. If anyone stared – and many people didn't even bother – it was with distrust and unwelcome. What was I doing, intruding on their poverty? I should go back to my tourist traps, meet more cadres' children and chat about pop music. I wondered if Paul had come riding here, and felt his dream of China corrode in the acrid, overpowering atmosphere of urine, river pollution and rotting food.

I took refuge in the old temple of Confucius, to the north.

I wanted to talk to someone, but the place was deserted. Who cared about Confucius, anyway? Modern ideas couldn't solve Beijing's problems – how could ideas two thousand five hundred years old? ('Man hasn't changed,' I muttered to myself.)

'I've just been to Qufu,' I said to the girl polishing trinkets in the temple gift shop.

'Where's that?' she replied.

'Qufu – where Confucius came from.'

'Oh, him.' She went back to her polishing, with the same look of arrogance as the young café-goers in Hangzhou. ('Man changes every moment – ask us, the fashion-conscious.')

It was with a sense of total emptiness that I pedalled on to the Bamboo Garden Hotel, where I stopped for a coffee and a pointless, deliberate wallow in the past evil of this place, now a pretty tourist trap but once the home of Kang Sheng, head of Mao's secret police. Then I rode towards the capital's ruined drum tower – the very thought of which made me long to be back on Queli Jie. But even if I were there, the game was over. Yes, travelling was a magical experience – the magic of the illusionist: thrilling, till one day you see the card being slipped up the sleeve or the false bottom in the top hat. Which is what had just happened to me. The only place I could go back to now was Guangzhou, to buttonhole new arrivals and warn them: 'Don't be fooled, about China or about yourself . . .'

'*Xuegao* [ice cream]!' a voice shouted. The old tower was surounded by a market, with peasants squatting behind sacks of produce. Against the walls leant the bikes on which they had pedalled their goods in from the country. Just a bike ride away . . . Their city customers haggled eagerly, their Beijing accents twanging like jew's-harps.

'*Xuegao!*' But what I wanted was a beer. A wooden stall with a sun-awning of old sacks was selling bowls of the stuff, cheap and sweet, the way it had been in Suzhou. I ordered and sat drinking at the shop's one table, observing and and being observed, giving and getting the pleasure of curiosity.

'*Xie!*' A new cry – 'Shoes!' – from a ragged man who had slouched into view under a shoulder pole. An iron sewing machine hung from one end, a stool and a canvas bag from the other. No wonder he was bent forward under that weight.

'*Xie!*' He laid down his burden and sank on to the bank by the tower wall, closing his eyes and letting a smile of relief cross his lips. Then he sat up and shouted again.

'*Xie!*' Nobody took any notice, apart from me. I wanted desperately to give this man some work but my proudly simple traveller's gear was all in perfect condition. Damn my pride . . . My mind raced, then I found myself calling out to him.

'You want a drink?'

He looked at me suspiciously. Maybe he hadn't understood, or maybe I was transgressing some Chinese code.

'Beer?' I said, and he turned away: my offer lapsed in mutual embarrassment.

'*Xie!*' He stuck around for a few more minutes, then trudged off. No business here, only a gibbering foreigner. His cry vanished down an alleyway, leaving me writhing with pity and anger. A new anger. That ragged, yoked man had managed a smile as he lay on the bank for his moment of rest. And there I had been, shouting and sulking because I hadn't got my spiritual goodies the second I wanted them. I was here, in the capital city of China, with only a few days to gorge myself on all it had to offer. Which wasn't its dead old tourist sites – it never had been, not to the real traveller – but its people and their lives. And my life, to be enriched, enhanced, made deeper and fuller . . .

I rode back past Tiananmen Square, where a bestiary of kites had taken to the skies. Stalin was just a picture on a hoarding; these were reality – here, now. Dragons, eagles, butterflies: as I stood watching them wheel above my head, I reflected on the greatest irony of travelling. How much the poor give to the rich.

'You'll love it.'

Brett looked doubtful, but he had come this far, so he joined me in the disorderly queue of men and women, many in Mao suits.

'Fifty fen,' said the ticket vendor. We paid and walked into an auditorium already packed with spectators – all Chinese, except for a row of exhausted American group-tourists on display in the front row. The house was buzzing with excitement: this was a night for drinking beer, cracking jokes, laughing, spitting, pointing at the *waiguo ren* . . . By ten to, there wasn't an empty seat left; at seven sharp the lights dimmed to one spot. A man in a yellow robe bounced into the cone of light, his face made up into hollow, startled monkey eyes and a mischievous monkey grin. When he opened his monkey mouth to sing, a shriek burst out as if a demon were being released. A fiddle squealed in terror. Percussionists began thrashing cymbals and drums to scare it away. Another demon cry followed, as devilish as the last.

'This is opera?' Brett hissed.

'Yes,' I replied, entranced. A second figure entered, in a massive headdress of pom-poms, jewellery and undulating pheasant feathers. The monkey-man greeted him by somersaulting across the stage to the accompaniment of ululating, high-pitched gongs. The Americans slumped forward in their seats. Brett groaned.

'The Chinese don't seem to think much of this, either,' he added. 'Look at them, chattering away to each other. They're as bored as I am.'

I glared and told him to shut up, but privately had to admit that my companion had a point: the auditorium was still a farmyard of noise. Paper bags rustled, beer bottles popped open, children chased up and down the aisle.

'You're the only one enjoying it,' he continued.

'No thanks to you.'

A man strode on in platform shoes, with huge flags sprouting out of his shoulders like banderillas. A cat-eyed woman and a chalk-visaged old man began arguing with him. '*Haaaa!*' Monkey-man popped up from behind the one stage prop, a wooden box. The gongs began again, a gorgeous, incomprehensible delirium of noise.

The interval came in no time – for me – but Brett gave another yawn and said he was leaving. The Americans trooped out, too, shell-shocked, trying to steel themselves for another day's hard leisure tomorrow. The Chinese? I thought of those infantile visitors to the Temple of Heaven – maybe this pageant really meant nothing to them. Then I thought of that itinerant cobbler and the kites over Tiananmen. China wasn't dead spiritually – I knew.

'Can I join you?' The voice came from behind.

I spun round, to see the cadre's son from the Qiaoyuan smiling at me.

'George! What are you doing here?'

'Same as you,' he replied. 'Enjoying the opera. Isn't it great?'

'Yes, but – I thought you were a rock fan. "Stairway to Heaven" . . .'

'I am.' He sat down in Brett's old seat. 'But this is my first love, Beijing opera. I've grown up with it – the stories, the singers . . . If I had a voice like Zhang, I'd quit rock tomorrow. And my studies, with that good job at the end. Have you been following the plot?'

'Sort of . . .'

He began explaining how the monkey-man had come to a feast in the Palace of Heaven, and upset the emperor and the courtiers so much with his fooling that a whole army was after him.

'Monkey is the people's hero,' he went on enthusiastically. 'He pokes fun at the authorities, and gets away with it.'

'Great,' I said, suddenly embarrassed at the disrespectful noise going on all around me. 'But, well, why aren't the people reacting?'

George burst out laughing. 'You Westerners! Sitting there so gravely . . . This was written to be performed in a marketplace: the singers had to scream to be heard, and if the audience didn't like them, they'd get a faceful of rotten fruit. It's the way I imagine rock concerts to be. Loud, lively, lots of energy.'

The lights began to dim again. During the second half, my young companion plied me with information.

'Watch the gestures they make with those long, hanging sleeves. There are more than fifty, each one with a different meaning. That guy folding the ends, he's a cheat.

'That woman always plays *hua dan* – young girls with spirit. During the Cultural Revolution, they broke her wrists and locked her in a cellar for a year.'

Anger welled up inside me – at the perpetrators and their apologists – then acrobats bounded on to the stage and blasted this negativity away. This was a celebration of life, uncrushable and glorious, 'with spirit'. No wonder the Red Guards had loathed it; no wonder it had survived.

'Now Monkey is surrounded,' said George. 'This is the

climax. Those men with flags represent armies: each one is a thousand soldiers. Against one guy. But watch!'

A weaponless sword fight followed, to manic orchestral accompaniment; then the people's hero somersaulted backwards over the heads of his opponents and was gone. The emperor let out a squawk of anger. The company turned towards us and began applauding, and the audience clapped and shouted back. The hall emptied slowly and noisily, George and I being among the last out.

'Wonderful!' I said.

'Glad you like it,' he replied. 'I feel proud when I see our opera, but sad when visitors come and don't understand.'

'It's not easy,' I said.

'Some people don't try.'

Don's voice came back again – 'What did you expect?' – and I nodded.

We walked to the bike park in companionable silence, stopping by a shining new Honda scooter.

'Have a drink before you go,' I suggested.

George tapped his watch. 'Gotta get home. My parents . . .' Half American teenager, half Confucian son, he climbed on to his machine and kick-started it into life.

'*Zaijian!*'

'*Zaijian!*'

The night streets were quiet and poorly lit. I pedalled slowly towards the Qiaoyuan, monkey-man and cat-woman still howling at each other inside my head. A waxing moon bowled along the rooftops beside me – when I next saw it this size, I would be in London. So I had to make the most of now . . . Now: the rickshaw men dozing in their vehicles; the cyclists jangling out of the half-light; the half-empty buses heading off for unknown destinations. China filled me with its glorious strangeness again – I had been forgiven.

11

A View from a Mountain

Beijing in a downpour. Cyclists in shining black kagoules vanished into a mist of spray; lines of identical apartment blocks had damp stains creeping down their sides like fungus. This image of uniformity, greyness and poverty was the China I had been warned about. And today of all days, the day we were going to the Great Wall . . .

'Traffic's bad, isn't it?' I said to Cheng, the driver, as we tagged ourselves on to another jam.

He nodded. 'Always is when it rains.'

We remained static for at least ten minutes, then crept forward a couple of vehicle lengths.

'It can take two hours to get out of the city,' he added. 'At least.'

'We've got all day.'

'I'm due back at six. No later.'

'Yes, well, that's still plenty of time. Isn't it?'

'Maybe. Of course these vans weren't designed for mountain roads – especially in this rain. There have been quite a few breakdowns recently.'

'Oh?'

'This one's due for a service.'

'What's he saying?' asked someone in the party. (I was the only Mandarin-speaker among them.)

'Nothing,' I replied, not wishing to increase the atmosphere of gloom.

It had seemed such a good idea. A small group, not one of those faceless coach trips, and an unusual destination: Mutianyu, up in the Yanshan mountains, not boring old Badaling, where everyone else went to see the Wall. But now . . .

'So cheer up!' said Brett.

'Yeah,' added Erik, shaking his head with his usual intense seriousness. Andy and Jane, two Oxford law students, began giggling at him.

The rest of the group, who had seemed so jovial last night, just kept rubbing the condensation off the windows and staring out at the weather. Emma, a teacher from New Zealand; two more Danes whose names I never found out; Scott and Sally, two Canadians too engrossed in each other to communicate with anyone else.

'It's like the July rains in Japan,' said Andy. Several others nodded.

'What's Japan like?' I asked.

'Wet.'

The vehicle ahead moved forward another handful of yards. Cheng put our bus into gear to follow, and stalled the engine.

Once on the capital's ring-road, the congestion eased. We sped past the gates of the Beijing Hilton and Holiday Inn, then a six-lane highway took us out into the country, to rejoin the company of carters, mule-drivers and coolies with shoulder poles. The rain was as hard as ever, drenching these people as thoroughly as it had their ancestors. Thousands of years of toil and discomfort . . .

Cheng pointed to a cassette player in the dashboard.

'You like?' He took a tape from the glove compartment and inserted it – Teresa Teng. I sat back and smiled: it reminded me of Shandong. Everyone else started to complain.

'Can you ask him to play something better?'

'Yeah, this is crap.'

Erik was digging in a day-pack. 'I've got some tapes.'

I replied that we ought to listen to Chinese music; Emma agreed, but a vote was taken, which the Sinophiles lost eight to two. We drove across northern Hebei listening to Pink Floyd. *The Wall*, of course.

The title track, whose lyrics equated formal education with

brainwashing, was particularly inappropriate. Since Confucius (and probably before), education had been the backbone of Chinese civilization. Young Hong Xiuquan had pursued it with so much zeal that it had driven him mad. The men and women sploshing past us would give anything to acquire it for their children. 'He that works with his mind shall rule,' Mencius had said in 350 BC. 'He that works with his hands shall be ruled.'

A man pulling a cart stuck his head through his tarpaulin-cum-anorak and began nodding in time to the beat that we were blaring out at him.

'Don't listen!' I shouted. He furrowed his brow and returned obediently to his own work-rhythm, while I wound shut the window – our only source of ventilation – angry and embarrassed. Was this all we could offer China in return for its gifts of fortitude and integrity? Self-pity and adolescent anarchism: luxuries even more insidious than the Coke bottles and scooters on the roadside hoardings.

The thin, grey line of the left-hand horizon slowly began to bulge up into hills wrapped in scarves of mist. Was it up there? Then we turned on to a side road and were heading straight for them. The bus dropped through its gears and started to whine up a series of hairpin bends. Cheng looked grimmer than ever, but we were too busy scanning the skyline to worry. One of us would be the first to spot the Wall.

We rounded another bend. Perhaps we'd suddenly pull in, Cheng would point to a lump of stones and that would be it. The Great Wall might be no more inspiring than the Forbidden City or the Temple of Heaven. It was two thousand years old, after all: we should think ourselves lucky there was any of it left.

'Look!'

Erik was jabbing at the glass with his finger. Even the Oxonians lurched across to his side.

'Up on that ridge!'

Nine pairs of eyes followed his gestures to a point far higher than the rest of us had dared look, where a string of square black towers threaded briefly out of the fog. Between them, suspended like bunting, hung the crenellations of the Great Wall of China.

'How the hell did it get up there?' someone whispered.

'Hard work,' Emma replied. 'Thousands of people died building that thing.'

I nodded: another monument to fear, power and brutality; another Nanjing. But it was so beautiful. A few more bends and we pulled into a bus park.

'The rest of the journey has to be made on foot,' said Cheng, pointing up into the mist. It was the first time I had seen him smile.

'Wow!' said Erik.

The students giggled again. Everyone else just stood and stared. A rockface tumbled away in front of us, hundreds of feet down into a scrubby, boulder-strewn valley. Behind us was the path – almost as steep – which we had just finished climbing. To either side of our vantage point, battlements and towers shinned up ridges and vanished into the unending flow of low, black clouds from the south. For the fortifications this was a low point; for any traveller, this was a high to treasure – their first steps on to the Great Wall.

'I think it's a disappointment,' said Andy. 'When we went trekking –'

'I think it's bloody marvellous,' I snapped. 'Come on, who's going which way?'

Nobody moved.

'Left?'

Heads began to shake.

'Right?'

Various objections were voiced: it was cold, people had done this sort of thing before. Only Erik remained silent.

'Come on, Erik.'

The one man who had aimed his look high enough to spot the Wall puckered his brow. Even he seemed to have run out of willpower.

'It'll be fun!' I said, with a sudden lack of conviction.

'No. I, er . . .'

I set off alone.

'Hello!' said the voice.

But there wasn't anybody about. There hadn't been anyone

for ages, only this tunnel of grey, these slippery, rough-hewn steps and these few yards of scrubby mountainside that the mist allowed me to see. I stopped to listen – for footsteps, for breathing – but heard nothing. Just the rain battering the rockface – harder than ever, it seemed. That voice? I must have imagined it. I resumed my climb, wondering what it must have been like to guard this huge, dark wall in weather like this. In winter, when the snow was –

'Hello!'

That was real enough. I shouted back, and got no response. Was somebody playing a game? Or was there a more sinister explanation? A squall rattled across the walkway behind me, and I was suddenly absurdly afraid. Emma had been right, back there in the comfort of our bus: thousands of slave labourers had died building this thing. Thousands of soldiers had died defending or attacking it. Older Chinese still believed it to be haunted by their spirits, by Qin Shihuang and by Qin's wall-builder, General Meng Tian (who had committed suicide because a geomancer told him that his wall had destroyed China's *fengshui*).

'Hello!'

I jumped, then told myself not to be so silly. A tower was visible through the mist, its arched door and windows configured like a leering, haughty face. From one of its eyes, a man was leaning and waving.

'Hello!' I shouted back.

'Come and drink with us!' he said, raising a bowl to his lips.

I hesitated. I had come here to explore, not to booze. But excuses for agreeing crowded into my mind: the weather, the visibility, the gnawing isolation of the walkway . . .

'*Ganbei!*' the man shouted.

That magic word!

'*Ganbei!*' I replied.

His group had taken over a bare, musty armoury and turned it into a place of warmth and welcome. They made me a space in their circle of spread-out raincoats, holding out a brown bottle of weak beer and a chicken leg wrapped in a page of the *People's Daily*. ('New Tractor Factory Opens in Shandong Province,' the headline ran. Ah well, so be it . . .) They fired the usual questions at me, a ritual which by now I thoroughly enjoyed. Don had promised I would come to feel that way about these interrogations – they were good-hearted, the interest was genuine; only linguistic competence was lacking (and travellers have no right to complain about that). I replied with my own questions, no doubt just as predictable. I learnt that my hosts were from a textile mill in the south of Beijing; that they were all in their twenties but still single; that this outing was part of the 'cultural and patriotic education' which they received from their work unit, and which none of them took very seriously.

'Who wants to see a lot of old stones?' said a red-faced man.

'It's your national monument!' I replied. 'Aren't you proud of it?'

'Not really. But it's a chance to get out of the factory for a day, so we're not arguing.'

The woman next to me nodded. 'America,' she said. 'That's where I'd like to go. My boyfriend's from America. Look, I've got a photo of him.' She reached into the pocket of her jacket and pulled out a plastic wallet. 'Rick. He's in computers. High technology. That's the future. Not this old place.'

The Wall stretched out ahead of me, glistening like a newly sloughed snake with the recently finished rain. I gave another wave to my friends in the armoury, then began climbing. A marvellous view had opened up with the retreat of the low cloud: axeheads of Mongolian rock stabbing up at the sky; the rich, terraced hills of China rolling away towards the wheat plains. Between them, the Wall reared up to cross a crest, then dipped out of sight; when it reappeared, it was in its unrestored state, gap-toothed and crumbling, struggling up the side of an enormous grey-green cliff to what was left of a watchtower. That tower had one remaining archway; it stared out across northern Hebei like the eye of a Buddha, all-seeing, all-knowing. I had to get there!

A loudspeaker that had seeded itself among the mountainside thorn trees began yapping instructions.

'One: do not drop litter!'

'Two: do not deface the monument!'

Despite the glorious view, I could see why the young textile workers were so indifferent. I thought of Miss Wei's comment: 'You'll be a child for the rest of your life.'

'Three: urinate only in the lavatories provided!'

'Four . . .'

I accelerated my pace to escape from this trivial bossiness as soon as possible. I was soon at the crest, looking down on a wall that degenerated into rubble, saplings, disorder and freedom. It was unspeakably inviting.

Then I saw it. A notice, in four languages: NO VISITORS BEYOND THIS POINT. The last restored tower was barred shut, its door and windows breezeblocked up, top to bottom. Barbed wire wound down the sides and along its roof. The only way past was to jump thirty feet on to bare, wet, jagged rock.

My archway might as well have been on the moon.

I walked slowly back to the armoury. Nobody was surprised.

'See what I mean?' said the man with the red face as I told my story. 'Have another beer.'

'Of course,' he added as I began drinking, 'if you really want to get up there, you can climb down the Wall.'

'Down the Wall? It's sheer –'

He took me to a window. 'Look!' A series of protruding blocks made a makeshift ladder down to the mountainside, where an indistinct, overgrown path wriggled back up the hill. 'We'd get into trouble if we went up that way,' he added. 'You'll be fine.'

I felt sickened at my privilege, but he just laughed.

'But we don't want to, so that's no problem.'

Dilapidation gave the Wall more majesty, not less. Birch trees might be growing out of its tumbledown flanks and grass might have overrun its walkway, but these flesh wounds only made it look doughtier than ever. It was the perfect companion for adventure. I turned round to look back at that blocked-up tower – way behind me, now – then ahead at the grey-green cliff and its ruined tower, right at the top. To the left, on the horizon, a streak of sunlight was visible, like light under a door: even the weather seemed to be on my side.

I glanced at my watch and began slipping and stumbling

upwards, more determined than ever to reach my goal. And as I climbed, the 'door' of the high cloud began swinging open, rolling back to reveal pure, blue sky. I had to give all my attention to crossing a crazy, fairground scree-slope, and when I looked up again, the whole far plain was shining silver and gold. The light grew nearer and nearer – into the foothills, over the first mountains – until I could see the faint circle of the sun through the cusp of the retreating cloud. A few seconds later, its full brightness struck my tower and flooded down into the valley. Spring came in an instant. Before I could adjust my eyes, steam was dancing off rocks that had been grey and cold. The Wall had turned from uniform brown to pink, black, sepia and umber. Insects had awoken and purple pasque flowers flung themselves open; 'green' vegetation was a hundred shades of colour. And the summit suddenly felt within easy reach. Ten more minutes . . . five . . . I was there.

An avalanche of blocks led through a breach in the Wall: a few scrambling steps and I was standing in the old window arch, gazing out over the finest view I had ever seen. The Great Wall of China tumbled away beneath my feet, sweeping through the barbed wire and loudspeakers of the tourist section in a moment, then climbing disdainfully back into the mountains, wild and free again. An arc of granite pinnacles stood watching in admiration; behind them, more peaks, row upon row, faded to blue as they crowded forward to catch a glimpse too. On the other side, across a void which would have swallowed a range of English mountains, those rich, sculpted hills flowed away in a perfect diminuendo, resolving to an infinitesimal haze, the smallness of the furthest ones testifying to their immense distance. Behind me, the Wall fell into a dip, then scuttled out of sight across a ridge of sheer grey triangles – keen, perhaps, to prepare in private for the greatest part of its Long March. Two thousand miles, across Shanxi, Shaanxi and Gansu, to the desert fortress of Jiayuguan.

Only an action could express the exultation that filled me. I grabbed a stone and hurled it towards the sky, watching it curl through space and plummet into the valley all those hard-won feet below. On landing, it refused to abandon its energy: striking bare rock, it sprang back up into the air, and my spirit leapt with it.

That moment – I knew at once, though don't ask me how – was what I had come travelling for. Those random rushes of pure, inexplicable happiness – in railway halts, on sacred hillsides, at temple gates – all suddenly acquired purpose and direction: to bring me here, now, to an archway on the Great Wall of China, to an instant of absolute joy and absolute certainty. For a time too short to measure, I shed every vestige of separateness and fused seamlessly with the world around me. I was caught up in the tumultuous swell of celebration that was pouring forth from every living thing, rejoicing at the simplest, most obvious fact imaginable: that they – that we – were alive.

'We're alive!' That was all. Nothing else mattered. How could it? No explanations were necessary, life was a miracle, beyond explanation. No meanings – life brought its own meaning, complete in itself. It was the 'uncarved block', whole and perfect.

Alive . . .

My stone hit the ground again. This time, it clattered to a stop. As the sound of its movement died away, I blanched with shame – to think I had once considered mankind to be subject to similar laws of entropy! But now I knew better. History did make us what we were – not the history of a few millennia, but the history of life: three billion years of evolution, of the most astounding creative adventure imaginable. This was a history that broke all rules – a history of perpetual newness and experiment, beginning with nothing but a dead sea of amino acids and building up step by step into our dazzling living world, into the 'myriad creatures'. It was a story of patience, of determination – above all, of generosity: to make it possible, 'uncarved' Nature had torn herself apart and given a share of herself to each of her creations. Hence that cry: the great world-creating force was all around me – in the grass rooting itself into the old wall, in the insects mating on a rock nearby, in the birds wheeling a thousand feet below me. And in me, in man . . . Perhaps most of all in man: we were the boldest experiment in the whole, vast saga; Nature's closest self-portrait, the most inquisitive, innovative and resourceful of all her creations. Like her, we human beings broke rules; we experimented, suffered and triumphed. We made the world, too, minute by minute.

As I reached out to pick up another missile, I felt my body fill with delight at its movements – my stretching arm; my grasping, searching fingers. This joy was my birthright, my covenant, my fortress of knowledge and value. No artificial powers could take it away – no emperors in 'forbidden cities', no pedlars of 'social forces' or 'historical inevitability'. It was unconditional and inexhaustible (just as Lao Zi had promised): it welled up from deeper inside than I had ever dared look. And it cried out to be recognized and expressed, for one silent, momentary roar of celebration to be translated into a lifetime of creativity and action.

I punched the air and shouted with involuntary triumph. 'We're alive!'

My cry merged again with the song of the living world. Then I let my words turn to curses at whatever had kept me cut off from the core of my being for so long. Then to thanks for whatever force had broken down those barriers. And finally to wonderment at what that force might be – for I could never have got here by myself. Suggestions crowded in, none of them satisfactory: that old God of guilt and self-hatred; that most Chinese of guardian angels, luck. Not even the wise words of Lao Zi were enough on their own. But for the first time, my ignorance didn't matter. It was enough to have felt what I had felt, to know what I knew.

So I just sat down and watched the few stray clouds float shadows across the spines and ridges of the Yanshan: fulfilled, triumphant, humbled and in love with the world – a traveller that had found absolute rest.

'Enjoy yourself?' said Andy as I climbed on the bus and took the last seat.

I couldn't think of a suitable reply.

'We've been waiting here for bloody ages. The driver's furious.'

'It's only ten past,' I snapped. 'He's got no right to complain.' Anger rose in me, then fell away, replaced by a gentle, inner voice of self-reproach.

'Sorry,' I said.

Cheng responded with another of his scowls, adding that in order to get to the depot in time, he would have to listen to his music all the way home, at full volume.

'I can't concentrate otherwise,' he explained, shoving Teresa Teng into the machine before any of us could question his logic.

'It's all your fault,' Jane muttered. 'What on earth did you find to do up there?'

Back on the plain, I stuck my fingers in my ears and stared out of the window in perfect tranquillity, watching the men and women of Hebei coming home from their fields, now bathed in the evening sunshine. How similar my first views of the People's Republic had been, of Guangdong's rice paddies, two thousand miles to the south. I had fallen in love with this land then, though I had needed time and help to overcome my expectations and prejudices. I needn't have worried. China, supposedly so xeno- phobic and ungiving, had been patient and generous, sharing freely her wisdom, her beauty, her richness and her poverty. And, as true lovers should be, I had been rewarded with a gift beyond the reach of all solitary striving – a glimpse into the universal Middle Kingdom of the human spirit. No lover, no pilgrim – no traveller – could have asked for more.

12

The Happy Traveller

Wong Meili – Amelia to her Western friends – broke off from clearing up the mess left by a party of backpackers and peered over my shoulder. 'What are you drawing?' she asked.

'A penguin,' I replied. 'P-e-n-g- . . .'

She took out her vocabulary book, wrote the word down in her slow, looping longhand, then walked around muttering it to herself: 'Pen-gu-in. Pen-gu-in.'

I wiped my brow for the hundredth time and got back to work.

I was in the south again, eighty miles from the Tropic of Cancer. In front of me, a sun-bleached, cobbled street led down to a shimmering river, the Lijiang, where men on bamboo rafts were punting passengers across to the huts, banyans and banana groves on the far bank. Behind them, huge willow-capped fingers of limestone pointed up at a Shandong-blue sky. This was the Middle Kingdom of Western and Chinese dreams, of tourist brochures and Tang dynasty silk painting. Could there be any better place to end my journey?

Amelia smiled again. 'More tea?'

'Oh, yes please.'

The beak – that was the difficult bit.

A two-day train ride south from Beijing had taken me to Guilin, ninety miles upriver from here. Guilin! There had been a picture of it behind the bar in the Qiaoyuan, showing round, fluted rocks gazing at their reflections in dream-still water; I had thought of that picture all the way across Henan and Hubei, as rice had replaced wheat, as water-buffalo had replaced tractors, as the air had grown ever hotter and damper. Then I'd arrived, in an ugly, dirty city debauched by tourist money, where coffee bars blared rock into litter-strewn streets and touts hassled scruffy, bored Westerners. There was even a café called McDonalds, where I paid home prices for a beer and sat next to an Australian who did nothing but boast about his sexual exploits.

'They're all on the game, the girls in the big hotels. Though you can get it for nothing if you play your cards right. It's hardly worth the bother. They're not a passionate people, the Chinese. Now, the Thais . . .'

I thought of all the emotions I had encountered on my journey among these 'not passionate' people, and concentrated on enjoying the beer. Next day, the first bus for Yangshuo had put me down in the village's tiny dust-bowl depot – at noon, when the temperature was over a hundred and the humidity only a little less. I staggered through empty *hutongs* to the nearest hotel, where I lay watching a gecko crawl round the ceiling above my head; only in early evening did I venture out for a walk (though the air was still like a steam bath). The Happy Traveller Café had no muzak, just bare walls and metal tables. Two backpackers sat sipping tea; Amelia, the proprietress, was busily sweeping the floor.

A day later, I was still here. The penguin – once I got it right – would go on the fridge. Then there were some English menus to do, and some posters to put round the walls. It seemed a tiny way of paying back China for all it had given me.

I finished my drawing – the flippers weren't quite right, either, but so what? – while Amelia went down to the river to bargain with one of the cormorant fishermen. (I had watched them at work the previous night: the birds had string tied round their gullets to stop them swallowing, and were sent into the water to haul out fish, which they did with astonishing grace and regularity.) We dined that evening by candlelight, eating steamed bass with Chinese onion and ginger, to the background of a million cicadas and next-door's TV.

'So, tell me about yourself,' I began (we'd had so little chance to talk during the day).

She shrugged. 'I'm nobody special.'

'Everybody's special,' I replied. It sounded trite, but I knew it wasn't.

The candle flickered. We ate a little more.

'You're an entrepreneur, right?'

'Oh, yes. Me and my uncle from Hong Kong, who lent me the money. But there are lots of us in China now – nothing special about that. "Grow rich through labour!", that's what the government says.'

'And are you growing rich?'

She tugged at the silk blouse she had put on for the occasion. 'But there's still a long way to go. They're making private cars in Shanghai. When I get one of those, then I'll be rich.'

Maybe then she'd regard herself as 'special' – a status symbol was about the only use for a car round here, with one metalled road in the whole of Yangshuo county.

'Tell me about your family,' I said.

'My parents were factory workers in Guangzhou. They've retired now, and I have to look after them; I'm the only child. Now, anyway – I had an elder brother, but he was sent to build highways in Tibet during the Cultural Revolution. He died in 1971. My parents don't approve of my dealing with Westerners. "Why can't you cook meals for Chinese?" they ask. But they accept the money I send them.'

'Would you rather prepare meals for Chinese? If the money was right?'

'Oh, no,' said Amelia. 'I get people from all over the world coming here.' She was a traveller, too, heading west rather than east.

I asked if she had a boyfriend, and she shook her head.

'No time,' she added, with an unconvincing laugh. Like all the best travellers, she journeyed alone. Hell, if that car would make her journey a little easier, who was I to criticize?

She went into her back room and reappeared with a bottle of plum liqueur. '*Gong hei fat choy!*' – May you make money! – was the Cantonese toast; Amelia grinned as we clinked glasses and drank. I wanted to say how much I admired her courage and enterprise; how, of all the people I had met in China – but someone began knocking at the back door.

'Who's there? Ah – Gu. Come in.'

The new arrival was a fat, bullet-headed man in his forties. The moment he saw me, his eyes lit up, and he began haranguing Amelia in dialect.

'He says he's doing a trip tomorrow,' she said. 'In his boat, the *Meihua*. To Xingping. He wants to sell you a ticket.'

'Is it worth going?' I asked, trusting that Gu spoke no English.

'Yes,' she replied hesitantly.

'Then I'll go.'

We haggled for a few minutes; the moment we had agreed a price, Gu left. Amelia looked relieved.

'It's a reasonable price,' she said.

'Fine. I'm looking forward to it.'

'It's very beautiful, our river. Though, well, his boat's not all that comfortable. Or clean . . . He's a powerful man, round here,' she added. (I thought of Gu Zhuquan, the famous Shanghai gangster. Any relation?) 'I know! You should take a bike and ride home. Borrow my Flying Pigeon. And don't let him charge you extra for it.'

When the meal was over, we chatted across a cup of 'real instant' coffee until Amelia began to look exhausted. I had watched her work all day, cooking, cleaning, shopping, book-keeping: maybe she was right about 'no time'. We stood up, and she stretched out a formal, nervous hand.

'*Zaijian.*'

'*Zaijian.*'

I walked back through the alleyways, happy to have eaten well, to have made a friend, to have done a useful day's work – above all, to be in China.

There were ten of us waiting on the quay. The river looked entrancing in the early light, so fresh and transparent, sparkling with innocence. The final traces of mist lurked under the huge mare's-tails that overhung the banks upstream; the sun was beginning to rise in the sky, ready to exorcize those last few ghosts of night and give us another scorching, clear day.

'Hrrumph!' A grimy cargo boat beneath us buried it all in a cloud of black smoke.

'Thank God we're not going on that!' one of the party exclaimed.

His wife looked at him contemptuously. 'No – a "cruise vessel", that's what the the man said.'

Gu appeared on deck. 'Come aboard!'

The couple were on the brink of a torrent of complaint; then a young New Zealander burst out laughing.

'Bicycles are extra,' said Gu as two Americans and I wheeled our machines down his gangplank. We pretended not to understand. The mate, a boy of about twelve, cast off fore and aft; the engine belched more pollution into the air. We nosed out into the tinkling current.

We soon realized that the *Meihua* was the ideal means of exploring the Lijiang. It was indistinguishable from the other trampships that ploughed up and down the busy waterway, so nobody paid any attention to it, even when we lay on the foredeck toasting ourselves in the sun. Children, normally eagle-eyed for foreigners, carried on their games of hide-and-seek along the banks. Fishermen on bamboo rafts kept hauling at their nets. Even the water buffalo in the shallows just looked up and gave a simple, dismissive snort.

And Amelia had been right about the destination. Those limestone buttes soon had us surrounded, each one a more bizarre shape than the last.

'That's called Maiden Looking in the Water,' said someone, pointing his guidebook at a sheer rockface of several hundred feet. 'And that one –' He pointed to a huge tricorn hat across the river from it. 'That's Scholar Contemplating the Moon. He's in love with the maiden, it says.'

'How bloody silly!' commented a fellow Englishman I was fast coming to dislike. 'They don't look a bit like scholars or maidens.'

I shrugged. Why shouldn't the Chinese poets who named these things be whimsical? Nature had been whimsical enough in creating these giant cones and cartoon bumps on the head, these cockscombs and blue-green bowler hats.

Between them and our river was a small strip of alluvial

land, where human needs were met effortlessly by Nature. Giant bamboos sprouted from the water's edge, the trunks strong enough to frame houses, the tops ideal for walling, furniture or fishing rods. Coconut palms fountained out of the shrubbery behind them – food, milk, roof thatch, ropes, matting, all from one plant. Bananas, jackfruit and oranges grew wild. Beneath us, the Lijiang teemed with fat, black fish. This was the jungle according to Rousseau – dreamlike and dripping with easy abundance. The few neat lines of maize outside the villages seemed unnecessary.

We groaned up a set of rapids – a man walking along the bank overtook us with ease – and rounded a headland. Ahead was a small, whitewashed town on a river confluence.

'Xingping,' said Gu.

So soon? The chatter of the engine faltered to a stammer, and we slid into the harbour, the mate emerging from his cabin to leap to the shore and make us fast.

'Taiping Heavenly Kingdom!' Two moon-faced boys bounded up as we disembarked, holding out fistfuls of coins.

The Englishman shooed them away, and we wandered into town, down an angular, white-walled *hutong* where it was hard to walk two abreast. It led us into a cul-de-sac, then into the courtyard of a laundry. Just as we were about to admit we were lost, we emerged in Xingping's main street – a cobbled road about as wide as a Cantonese alley, overhung with tin roofing, washing, and tottering brick balconies. Shoppers jostled along the middle, safe from the sun in their broad, conical hats. Along the sides, wherever there was shade, peasants sat with produce for sale: rice, shallots, lychees, walnuts, oranges, marrows, dried fish, duck chicks. Cars were totally absent; even the cyclists had to dismount and push through the mass of shoppers.

'Strawberry?' A young woman in pigtails was holding out a sample. They were green, hard and bitter, but I bought some anyway. It was worth it for the receipt, a brimming, toothy smile. A bakery offered us respite from the crowd and sold us a bag of soft, steamed sesame buns. At the end of a line of workshops and small businesses, we came to a restaurant.

'Lunch?' I suggested.

When ten foreigners walked into the Xingping Noodle House,

the proprietor almost dropped the fen notes he was counting in shock.

'I'd like to see a menu,' I said.

'No menu. Only noodles. Made here – yesterday! the boss replied, pointing through the back door at tomorrow's supply drying on a wooden frame, squared off like the warp on a loom. Most restaurant noodles came from packets, so this would be a treat.

'Haven't they heard of choice?' my compatriot huffed. I sat down, and a waitress went past with a couple of bowls. The indefinable smell of simple, well-made food filled my nostrils.

The best thing about this café, even so, was its décor. We were surrounded by posters – four walls of them, celebrating every aspect of Chinese life in strident, day-glo colours. Shanghai film starlets pouted their lips at me; young Mao strode across the mountains towards Anyuan; Emperor Qin Shihuang took flight on a winged horse to supervise the building of his wall. Confucius, Lao Zi and Buddha stood in a huddle, the Sage of Qufu rubbing his hands like a servile official and the founder of Taoism holding up a long-nailed index finger in inspiration. New Year greetings came from a dome-headed old man patting a baby on the head, for some reason accompanied by a giant fish. A sugary-eyed panda in a pair of games shorts invited teenagers to a national football competition. A wholesome-looking young woman in peasant dress held out a flower, luring me to the Tianshan Mountains. I'd go at once, but I had a flight home in a few days.

Here, captured and distilled in a way no conscious collection of imagery could have done, was my Middle Kingdom. The one I had found, not the one I had been told to expect: proud, brash and full of laughter, mysterious, secretive and tragic; tough and sentimental, ancient and novelty-struck – beyond all these paradoxes, a country perpetually in motion, gloriously, irrepressibly alive. If the posters around me reflected a truth I had been anticipating – that China was under the spell of conflicting, irreconcilable influences (modernity, tradition and Marx) – they also beamed out their own, higher truth: that this country was bigger than all these things. I thought of my fellow riders on the roads of Shandong, 'making do' with their bikes to transport everything that needed transporting. I looked out into the street, at the bustle and the bargaining, at the burgeoning sacks of produce and the eager customers. And I thought of the Great Wall (there was a picture of it here, lit in puce and turquoise), of one moment of wisdom . . .

Modernity, I knew, was inevitable. But did this mean that China's uniqueness was doomed? Tradition wasn't the brittle shell that some philosophers made it out to be. 'The limits of language are the limits of thought,' Wittgenstein had said – but I had learnt that the mind could burst out of those limits, not just to tumble down into madness but to ascend into wordless beauty and understanding. Tradition, like language, was not a barrier but an enabler, a vehicle for human creativity. With its help, the people of China were making their own solutions to the problems of change even now, as I sat here; not in committee or congress, but in their lives, in their billion difficulties and the billion different answers they would find to them. Tradition would alter in the process, but then it always had: it was never static, whatever the Sage of Qufu might have believed or wanted. Perpetual revolution was the human condition – not Maoist but Taoist: uncontrolled, unheralded, undetermined, with no end, and as many beginnings as there were human beings to initiate them.

But what of the third influence, Marxism? Here, doubt entered my mind. There they were, too, whisked from the top of Tiananmen Square to the exit of the Xingping Noodle House: Marx, Engels, Lenin and Stalin. Westerners, inflexible and fanatical, who knew they were right – how unlike Wang's wise man, bending like bamboo. Nobody could argue with the achievements of the Party since 1949 – the increased wealth, the improvements in health. But nobody could hide the darker side, either – the new religion, and the new inquisition that had come with it. These four men had claimed to know the absolute, in a far more ambitious way than Lao Zi or Wei Lang: they claimed to have grasped it in totality, to have stripped it to its workings and revealed it, logical and machine-like, for all to see. They had claimed that anyone who didn't see was blind or wicked. And one of them had cast tens of millions of human beings into the latter category, and exterminated them. The handsome, zealous young Mao Zedong had done the same, on a lesser (but still appalling) scale: 'Qin Shihuang only buried four hundred and sixty scholars,' he had once boasted. 'We buried forty-six thousand.'

All the bad memories from my journey suddenly came rushing back at me: Qingping, Zhu, Wang's story, the factory boss with his megaphone, those faceless guardians of Confucius' tomb . . . Man, that miraculous being I had discovered striding free along the Great Wall, could become a monster, smashing holy relics and opera singers' wrists, pummelling old teachers to death while laughing. Nature's living self-portrait could turn into a wanton destroyer, with a passion for violence far beyond its evolutionary need for self-preservation. Why? It happened whenever we divided humanity up into types, into classes or races, when we thought we knew who was good and who was bad. But why did we then turn so savage? Was this destructiveness some strange perversion of our creativity? (Wang had found liberation from selfhood, too – in Tiananmen Square, in mass hysteria.) Or had Nature played a cruel trick, implanting a pointless killer drive, like Freud's 'death instinct'? Or was there really a Devil, to go with that old-fashioned God?

The ghosts of history seemed to come swarming out of their hiding places again, as if my moment on the Wall had been an aberration, a hallucination caused by the mountain air and the work of climbing. I was back under the Taiping Gate, listening to a roll call of bloodshed: 1864, 1927, 1936, 1949. Man, a marvel? You must be crazy! I gazed helplessly round at my bright, cheerful walls, desperate for inspiration.

'Forget it! Have fun while you can,' said Teresa Teng.

'Men are just puppets,' muttered Marx.

'All men are evil!' boomed Qin Shihuang.

'Hurry up!'

It wasn't just the Brit complaining, this time. I ate my noodles as quickly as possible, with the speed and grace of a man trying to run on stilts. We paid (forty fen each) and walked back towards the waterfront.

'What's the matter?' asked one of my companions.

'Oh, nothing.'

We sat trying to eat those strawberries, while a ferryman

punted his boat back and forth across the river. He was never without a full complement of chattering, straw-hatted passengers. Life was going on all around me, ignoring my brooding and setting up a joyful, active rhythm. To be gloomy here was madness! Self-indulgence of the worst kind. Philosophers had grappled with the problem of evil for thousands of years and hadn't produced an answer: how could I? Instead, I had been granted a rare glimpse of its opposite. Wasn't that enough? To know that there was a fortress of good inside ourselves that could not be exhausted by use, only ignored by stupidity? So, we always had a fight on our hands, down here on the plains. So there was no simple, static, logical, Western-style answer to the deepest questions. 'Have in your hold the Great Image, and the Empire will come to you,' Lao Zi had promised, and I knew the Old One was to be trusted.

The *Meihua* let out a blast on its hooter: time to go back. We wandered down to the quay, where Gu helped me and two Americans to unload our bikes.

'Have a nice ride,' said the 'gangster'.

'*Taiping Tianguo!*' The boys were back. 'Fif'y fen! Cheap!'

It was money well spent. The blank brass disk made an appropriate memento of liberation.

There was only one road out of town, sporadically metalled; it took us up a rock knoll and down a long, straight valley flanked with twin colonnades of limestone. The sun shone on us with absurd generosity, filling the landscape with warmth and colour. A lark sang somewhere up in the sky; the young rice all around us glowed spring-green. 'Hello!' shouted a ploughman. This was my final encounter with the Chinese countryside; it felt like a triumphal procession, and I abandoned myself to joy.

That evening was my last in Yangshuo, my last hours in the Middle Kingdom not asleep or on the move. I walked round the town, quietly and alone, hoovering up impressions to take home: smells of cooking oil, smoke, drying fish and rotting fruit; sounds of cicadas, cage birds and cheap radios playing Taiwanese pop. An unlit bicycle came rattling towards me out of the darkness; a child pointed and laughed. '*Waiguo ren!*' God, I'd even miss the spitting . . . And on the waterfront, I found a crowd of people standing in silence, gazing intently out across the Lijiang.

'What's everybody here for?' I asked an American I recognized from the hotel.

'Full moon tonight.'

I joined the wake. For a long time there was nothing, just the lanterns of the cormorant fishermen and lights on the Guilin road. The river gurgled by, patient and unending, like the river of Chinese culture. Insects screeched and whined; I felt their bites, and was pondering the idea of returning to my bed. Then the American tapped me on the shoulder. Look! The clouds were parting.

A perfect silver circle rolled out and hurled a jet of dancing mercury across the water. Everybody – Westerners and Chinese in unison – gasped with delight, and for the last time on my journey I felt that overpowering instant of stillness and perfection.

If that wasn't knowledge enough, nothing could be.

I rose early next morning and packed, sauntering down to the Happy Traveller for a farewell breakfast. Amelia and I sat and talked about our ambitions: when I came back as a working, performing musician, I would be able to stay at the Happy Traveller Hotel, and she'd take me for a ride in that car. We almost believed ourselves.

Amelia's Golden Dawn alarm-clock gave the click it always made passing the hour. I was late.

'Well – 'bye 'bye.'

'Yes. 'Bye 'bye.'

But I couldn't just turn round and walk off. This wasn't just a friend I was saying farewell to, but a whole country, a place that had become a part of me. So I brushed Amelia's outstretched hand aside, and gave her a big warm hug and a kiss on each cheek. She tensed up at once; I let go and she backed away, suddenly shocked and insecure.

Two minutes past.

'*Zaijian!*' I tried to sound chirpy.

I had to go. I trudged off down the street, filled with disappointment that my last act before heading towards England should involve such utter misunderstanding. Then I turned round and saw my friend waving. Westerners heading east,

Easterners heading west: all that learning to do. We were so lucky.

In an hour's time I would be back at the border; a few hours to kill, then I'd be on my flight back to London. I gazed out of the train window at the rice fields and the sun falling through the palm groves, at the t'ai chi harvesters and those dead-straight dirt tracks that ran all the way to Shandong. How could I ever bear to leave them? London meant routine, an office, grey skies and cheerless streets; it meant bosses and subordinates, it meant having to impress and conform. Could I make it mean more, after all this? Dull Western things had given me the means and the time to visit the East – where I had learnt that the eyes of many Chinese were looking as eagerly west. Not just on our cars and videos, but on our freedom and individual responsibility. China had given me respect for my own culture, too.

But still . . . The land became rougher and turned into scrub. Those navvies were still hacking at the soil. Then the first tower blocks of Shenzhen Special Economic Zone came into view. That sense of impending loss, which had been clawing all morning at my stomach, was now as strong as fear. China had changed me so much: what would I do without it? Desperately I gazed round at the other passengers, at their black hair, round, flat faces and ill-matching Mao suits. The moment I lost the reality of this journey, I would have lost all the things I had come to value. What would I become? A travel bore, living for a photo album and a dog-eared diary – things that would grow staler and more ritualized every time I resorted to them? A man marooned in his own past, while the life he had so briefly transcended closed back over his head? I wouldn't even be able to lie to myself any longer that it was all great, that one couldn't hope for any more . . .

'*Jiangsi!*'

A chess match was finishing somewhere down the carriage. I thought of all the games I had played on my journey – that first train ride, Dr Cao's present, a temple gate in Shandong – and felt a great warmth flow into me. How absurd I was being! The reality of this journey was inside me: I hadn't just seen and learnt, I had become.

The train began to slow down. I tried flipping my backpack down from the luggage-rack, the way Marie-Claude had done: it caught on the edge and I lost my balance, sprawling across the table and sending a mug of tea crashing to the floor.

Before I came travelling again, I'd have to practise.

POSTSCRIPT

All stories have a twist to them, though I wish this one didn't.
Chinese you meet in 1991 refer to it as the 'Beijing event', and
hustle the conversation on to something else.

Like many Sinophiles, I watched the build-up of events in May
1989 with mounting excitement. The student movement was a
good example of the 'new China' I had met on my journey:
young, intelligent and patriotic; looking outward to the world
and forward to the future; idealistic but not ideological. I was
sure they would succeed – with a little diplomacy from the
students, with a little tolerance of teenage overzealousness from
their elders. How could they not? They were the cream of the
nation, its future. And the ordinary citizens of Beijing were
behind them, too; this wasn't just a movement of intellectuals,
but of *renmin*, the people.

There's no point in going over the story again. Choose your
own image. The goddess of democracy tumbling to the ground;
that young man standing in front of a line of tanks; those tents,
where sleeping teenagers were squashed to death . . .

So, was Zhu right after all? And David, with his remorseless
pessimism over that dinner in Guangzhou? My optimist's view
of China – a country worthy of, and in the process of, becoming
a great world nation – suddenly looked naive and obsolete. I
recalled all those well-meaning writers who had been to the
People's Republic in the Sixties and Seventies, and had been
duped into believing they had found a perfect society. Shirley
MacLaine, Abbie Hoffman – maybe I was just another sucker to
add to that list. Gloomier, more recent visitors had brought back
a China that was drab, surly, arrogant, cruel and dissembling –
the world's biggest banana republic. They'd got it right after all.

I went back through my text, looking for things that I could change – enthusiasms to water down; gestures and sayings to reinterpret; little time bombs of anger to plant. But, apart from slipping a couple of asides into the description of Tiananmen Square and changing a few names, I didn't find anything that I wanted to amend.

Real change was taking place in the China I visited, of a kind that cannot be halted. Political power does not always come out of the barrel of a gun (as Mao, who laid great stress on propaganda, knew full well). When I meet young Chinese in Britain – even those who provide excuses for the 'event' – I know that the China that I saw was real, that my Middle Kingdom has not ceased to exist.

It has, however, slipped temporarily out of view. This makes it all the more important to retain its image in our minds. We must not allow clichés of 'Oriental cruelty' to reassert themselves, to lull us into an acceptance that Tiananmen was 'inevitable' and that the passion for freedom and fairness that erupted in Eastern Europe has no place in eastern Asia. For each ageing, frightened leader and each mindless, obstructive Party hack, China has many kind, unpretentious, thoughtful individuals, who are eager for their country to enjoy prosperity, openness, order and justice. Passing on my encounters with a few of these latter people is now a duty as well as a pleasure. My journey to the Middle Kingdom was to their China, the China that will eventually emerge into the modern world through its superior moral force, humanity, industry and intelligence. I'm prouder than ever to have been there and seen it.

APPENDIX I
Pronunciation

Romanization is a problem that confronts all writers on the Middle Kingdom – how to transliterate strange, beautiful Chinese characters into dull, sensible Western letters. There are several competing systems: Harvard, Wade-Giles and Pinyin. I have chosen Pinyin, both because it is the one favoured in the People's Republic and because it is the most accurate – Beijing was always spoken 'Beijing', even when Wade and Giles were writing it 'Peking'. Here is a simplified, general table of pronunciation. In all cases, English equivalent sounds can really only be approximations; proper Chinese textbooks are full of diagrams and linguistics-speak ('"D" is an alveolar unaspirated voiceless plosive . . .')

q- is pronounced ch, as in 'chump'

x- is pronounced sh, as in 'sheep'

zh- is pronounced j, as in 'juniper'

-ou is pronounced oe, as in 'Joe'

-ian is pronounced yen, as in the Japanese currency

-eng is pronounced ung, as in 'sung' (at Oxford)

-ong is pronounced ung, as in 'sung' (in Yorkshire)

-e and -i vary in pronunciation, depending on what comes before.

APPENDIX II

Glossary and Word-by-Word Pronunciation Guide

In this, I have erred on the side of obviousness: non-Sinologists cannot be blamed for ignorance about a country that has been so secretive for four thousand years. Experts will, I'm sure, forgive me for telling them how to pronounce Wei Lang or who Liu Shaoqi was.

Anyuan	an-yuan	scene of successful miners' strike initiated by Mao in 1922
Badaling	ba-da-ling	most visited spot on the Great Wall
Beijing	bay*-jing	Peking (lit. 'northern capital')
bund		embankment by a river
bushi	boo-shuh	No
CAAC		China's airline. 'Always Cancels', according to backpackers
Cao	tsao	surname
cadre		top party official
cha	cha	tea
Cheng	chung	surname
county		administrative sub-unit of a province (e.g. Qufu county)
Cultural Revolution		ten-year upheaval (1966–76), launched by Mao but soon out of his (or anybody else's) control
Da Yunhe	da yun-huh	the Grand Canal (from Hangzhou to Beijing)
dajie	da-jee-ay	avenue
Daodejing	dao-duh-jing	(Wade-Giles *Tao Te Ching*). Sacred Taoist text, probably compiled over several centuries, c. 600 BC – 400 BC, though ascribed to Lao Zi
Daojiao	dow-jeeow	Taoism

*'ay' as in 'hay'

179

Dazhai	da-jai	exemplary commune, often cited by Mao
erhu	are-hoo	two-stringed violin
FEC		Foreign Exchange Certificate – money used in Friendship Stores and tourist hotels
fengshui	fung-shwei	the Taoist art of geomancy; the propitiousness of a site according to this art
Friendship Store		shop full of imported goods, for foreigners only (and Chinese with *guanxi*)
ganbei	gan-bay	cheers! (lit. 'Empty the glass!')
Gansu	gan-soo	northern province
Great Helmsman		one of Mao's titles during the Cultural Revolution
Great Leap Forward		disastrous agricultural reform of 1958–61, resulting in massive famine
guangchang	gwang-chang	square (as in Tiananmen Square)
Guangdong	gwang-dong	province around Guangzhou
Guangzhou	gwang-joe	Canton
guanxi	gwan-shee	contacts (in high places)
Guilin	gway-lin	tourist city in south China
Guomindang	gwo-min-dang	(Wade-Giles Kuomintang). Nationalists – enemies of Communists in Civil War, c. 1925–49
Han	han	dynasty (206 BC – AD 220). Also 'ethnic Chinese'.
Han China		central and eastern China
Han Fei	han fay	'legalist' (qv) philosopher, died 233 BC
Hangzhou	hang-joe	tourist city south-west of Shanghai
Hebei	huh-bay	northern province (Wade-Giles Hopei)
Hong Xiuquan	hung shiu-chuan	leader of Taiping ('Heavenly Peace') Rebellion, born 1814, died in siege of Nanjing, 1864
Hongqi	hung-chee	Red Flag, Chinese-made limousine
Hongwu	hung-woo	founder of Ming dynasty, noted for his ruthlessness (see Zhu Yuanzhang)

Huang He	hwang huh	Yellow River
huaqiao	hwa-cheeao	non-mainland Chinese
Huaxian	hwa-shyen	town in Guangdong province
Hunan	hoo-nan	poor, mountainous province in the south
Huqiu	hoo-cheoo	Tiger Hill, the emblem of Suzhou
hutong	hoo-tung	alley
jiangsi	jyang-suh	checkmate
Jiangxi	jyang-shee	another poor, mountainous province
jie	jee-ay	street
jiefang	jeeay-fang	liberation; as a date, 1949
Jinggangshan	jing-gang-shan	mountain range in south China
Journey to the West		one of the four Chinese classics, a mythological tale based on Xuan Zang's journey to India in the seventh century AD
Kangxi	kang-shee	Qing dynasty emperor (reigned 1662–1723)
Kong Fuzi	kung foo-zuh	Confucius (551 BC – 479 BC)
Lao Zi	lao zuh	(Wade-Giles Lao Tzu – lit. 'Old One') semi-mythical author of *Daodejing*
legalism		philosophy that preached the inevitability of human selfishness and the necessity of ruthless government
Lin Biao	lin biao	Mao's deputy during Cultural Revolution. Born 1907, died 'in plane crash' after attempted *coup d'état* 1971
Lingyan Shan	ling-yan	mountain, topped by a temple, near Suzhou
Lijiang	lee-jyang	river in south China
Liao	lee-ao	surname
Liu Bang	lew bang	peasant rebel, founder of Han dynasty (256 BC – 195 BC)
Liu Shaoqi	lew shao-chee	moderate Communist leader, born 1898, murdered in Cultural Revolution, 1974
lu	loo	1)road. Renmin Lu = People's Road 2)surname

Mao jacket		round-collared denim jacket, actually first popularized by Sun Yat Sen
Maotai	mao-tai	powerful alcoholic beverage
Mao Zedong	mao zuh-dung	Mao Tse-tung (1893–1976)
Meiguo	may-gwo	America
meiyou	may-yoe	no (in the sense of 'we haven't got any'). Catch-phrase of unhelpful officials
Mencius		Confucian philosopher (390 BC – 305 BC)
Meng Tian	mung tyen	Qin-dynasty general
Ming	ming	dynasty (1368–1644)
moon gate		circular gateway in ornamental garden
Mutianyu	moo-tyen-yoo	newly opened stretch of Great Wall, north-east of Beijing
Nanjing	nan-jing	Nanking (lit. 'southern capital')
ni hao	nee hao	hello
pijiu	pee-jeoo	beer (nicer than it sounds!)
PLA		People's Liberation Army
qi	chee	Life energy in Taoist medicine (the character also means 'air')
Qianmen	chyen-men	front gate of old Beijing
Qianlong	chyen-lung	Qing dynasty emperor (reigned 1736–96)
Qiantang	chyen-tang	river through Hangzhou
qilin	chee-lin	mythical beast, China's unicorn
Qin	chin	dynasty (221 BC – 207 BC), covering rule of Qin Shihuang
Qin Shihuang	chin shuh-hwang	Brutally effective first unifier of China. Builder of Great Wall
Qing	ching	dynasty (1644–1911)
Qinghai	ching-high	mountainous central province, reputedly the site of China's gulag
Qingping	ching-ping	animal market in Guangzhou
Qinian	chee-nyen	Hall of Prayer for Good Harvest, centrepiece of Temple of Heaven in Beijing
Queli	chwei-lee	street in Qufu
Qufu	choo-foo	birthplace of Confucius
Ren	ren	1)person

		2)the supreme Confucian virtue, of humaneness
renmin	ren-min	people('s)
renminbi	ren-min-bee	(lit. 'people's money'). Ordinary currency. 100 fen = 1 yuan, worth 20p of English money in 1985
Shaanxi	shan-shee	province (Wade-Giles Shensi)
Shamian	sha-myen	old European concession in Guangzhou
shan	shan	mountain(s)
Shandong	shan-dung	province (Wade-Giles Shantung)
Shanxi	shan-shee	province (Wade-Giles Shansi)
Shao Hao	shao hao	semi-mythical emperor, c. 2000 BC
shei a	shay ah	who's there?
Shenzhen	shen-jen	southern city, entry-point from Hong Kong
Sichuan	suh-chwanh	province (Wade-Giles Szechwan), noted for spicy food
Song	sung	dynasty (960–1279)
stele		stone tablet inscribed with religious text
Sui	sway	dynasty (581–618)
Sun Zi	sun zuh	Taoist military tactician, fl. c. 350 BC. He had a great influence on Mao's generalship
Suzhou	soo-joe	city north-west of Shanghai
Taihedian	tai-huh-dyen	Hall of Supreme Harmony in the Forbidden City
Taijiquan	tai-jee-chwan	(Wade-Giles T'ai-chi-chuan). System of exercise, involving meditation and martial art
Tangqiao	tang-cheeao	small town in Shandong province
Teresa Teng		Deng Lijun, Taiwanese pop-star also popular on mainland
Tianguo	tyen-guo	Heavenly Kingdom of Taiping rebels
Tianjin	tyen-jin	(Wade-Giles Tientsin). Port south of Beijing
Tiantan	tyen-tan	Temple of Heaven in Beijing
Tsingtao	ching-dao	(Pinyin Qingdao). China's best beer
Uygur	way-gur	Moslem minority people, from north-west

waiguo ren	why-gwo ren	foreigner
Wei	way	surname
Wei Lang	way lang	sixth Zen patriarch, also known as Hui Neng, 638–713 AD
Weiguo	way-gwo	patriotic given-name (lit. 'Protect the land')
Wu Wang	woo wang	King Wu, founder of Zhou dynasty (1027 BC)
Xia	shee-ya	dynasty (21st century BC – 1500 BC)
xiangqi	shyang-chee	Chinese chess
xie	shee-ay	shoes
Xihu	shee-hoo	West Lake, famous Hangzhou beauty spot
Xingping	shing-ping	small town on Lijiang River
Xishuangbanna	shee-shwang-ban-na	far south-western border area
xiuxi	sheeoo-shee	siesta
xuegao	shway-gao	ice cream
yamen	ya-men	government office
Yan'an	yan-an	(Wade-Giles Yenan). End point of Long March. Symbol of pure, early Communist idealism
yang	yang	male principle in Taoist cosmology
yang guizi	yang gway-zuh	standard Chinese insult to Westerners, meaning 'Foreign devil!'
Yangshuo	yang-shwo	small town on Lijiang River
Yangzi	yang-zuh	Yangtze River
Yanshan	yan-shan	range of mountains north of Beijing
Yanzhou	yan-joe	town in Shandong province
yin	yin	female principle in Taoist cosmology
Yingguo	ying-gwo	England
Yongdingmen	yung-ding-men	suburb of Beijing
Yue Fei	yoo-eh fay	Song dynasty hero executed on trumped-up charges of treachery
Yuhuatai	yoo-hwa-tai	hill south of Nanjing, site of a massacre of suspected Communists in 1927
Yunnan	yun-nan	south-western border province
zaijian	zai-jyen	goodbye

Zhang	jang	most common surname in China
Zhejiang	juh-jyang	province (Wade-Giles Chekiang)
zhenci	jen-tsuh	acupuncture
zhe shi ...	jay shuh ...	this is ...
zhongfan	jung-fan	lunch
Zhongguo	jung-gwo	China (lit. 'Middle Kingdom')
Zhongnanhai	jung-nan-high	part of Beijing where topmost leaders live
Zhou	joe	dynasty (1027 BC – 770 BC), a golden age of good government, according to Confucius
Zhou Enlai	joe en-lai	(Wade-Giles Chou En Lai). Chinese premier 1949–76 (lived 1898–1976)
Zhu	joo	surname
Zhuang	jwang	surname
Zhu De	joo duh	military commander on Long March
Zhu Yuanzhang	joo yuan-jang	renegade Buddhist monk (1328–98) who became a rebel leader and founded the Ming dynasty, taking the Imperial reign-title Hongwu

NOTE: In a Chinese name (Wang Weiguo) the surname comes first, the given-name second. The banners that greeted Hua Guofeng on a visit to Yugoslavia, with 'Comradely Greetings to Mr Guofeng!' on them, did not impress the guests.

Since 1949, women have kept their own names on marriage, for example, Mao's wife Jiang Qing.

APPENDIX III
A Brief Note on Traditional Chinese Religions

China has never had 'one' religion, in the manner of the West or the near East – instead, three separate doctrines have looked after different aspects of religious life. A Chinese friend gave me this formula for the way they interact: Confucianism tells us how to live with our fellow men, Buddhism how to live with God, Taoism how to live with nature. She went on to compare Chinese religion to one of those Shang dynasty sacrificial vessels that stands – as securely as ever after three thousand years – on three legs.

Confucianism is not really a religion, more a philosophy of society – but every town in Imperial China would have had its Confucian temple, and the Sage's spirit would often be invoked in moments of stress. Its concern was with political order, and it was upheld not by force, but by consent. Confucius's views on women and on commerce seem to me obsolete and unpleasant, but his views on individual duty and on the importance of general education and social consensus are as relevant now as they were in 500 BC. While the West makes wisecracks about 'Confucius, he say . . .', the countries of the Pacific rim put his more durable teachings into practice and boom economically.

Buddhism is, in essence, the simplest of the great religions – there is no God, only a ruthlessly logical law of karma by which souls shed the inevitably painful trappings of earthly life to achieve 'nirvana', or nothingness. By the time it reached China, however, it had developed competing schools of great complexity, many of which involved pantheons of spirits and daemons that would probably have appalled Gotama Siddhartha. The two branches that had most influence in the Middle Kingdom were Pure Land and Chan. 'Pure Land' is strangely reminiscent of Christianity – Buddha has become a loving God, surrounded by saints and angels; spirits of the dead go to heaven or hell (a Goddess of Mercy, Guanyin, will intercede, like Mary, for errant souls). Chan, 'Zen' in Japan, is a much purer form. Rather than a series of doctrines, it is a way of life, a set of techniques for acquiring religous enlightenment through flashes of insight. Its appeal to a Western world desperate for faith but helplessly unable to 'prove' the existence of the transcendental is obvious.

Tao ('Dao' in Pinyin, but the Wade-Giles 'Tao' is much more familiar in the West) is an unstructured mixture of philosophy, mysticism, magic and superstition. It is the source of traditional Chinese ontology – the belief that phenomena arise from the perpetual interaction of two opposing principles, *yin* and *yang*. Like early Buddhism, it denies the existence of an objective 'God'; instead, it teaches a kind of pantheism – that the process of this interaction is divine. Human development is largely about transcending our 'ego' to bring ourselves into harmony with this process. As in Zen, faith is not a matter of reason, but of intuition, carefully nurtured by appropriate practices and techniques. Appropriately, Taoism never developed a formal structure like China's other two 'legs' – the Taoists were always the outsiders, the opponents of authority and arbitrariness. Sometimes these outsiders were political rebels, other times saints, other times con-men (and -women). They were never dull, and provided Chinese life with an important antidote to the grey but worthy Confucians.

A fourth 'leg' has now been tacked on to the tripod: when people – especially top officials – die, it is said that they have 'gone to meet Marx'. My views on the permanence of this addition should be obvious from the text.

APPENDIX IV
The Main Chinese Dynasties

Xia	21st century BC – 1500 BC
Shang	1500 BC – 1027 BC

Earliest known Chinese characters found on 'oracle bones'

Zhou	1027 BC – 770 BC
'Spring and Autumn'	770 BC – 450 BC
Warring States period	450 BC – 221 BC

Two eras of strife between various Chinese states. But also the golden age of Chinese philosophy: Lao Zi, Confucius, Mencius

Qin	221 BC – 207 BC

Qin Shihuang first person to unite all China. Great Wall built

Han	206 BC – 220 AD

Confucianism becomes state ideology. Buddhism also introduced

'Three Kingdoms'	220 – 581
Sui	581 – 618

Grand Canal built

Tang	618 – 907
'Five Dynasties'	907 – 960
Song	960 – 1279

Golden age of Chinese technology and science

Yuan	1279 – 1368

Rule by Mongol invaders. Marco Polo at court of Kubla Khan

Ming	1368 – 1644

Conservative, inward-looking, autocratic regime. China begins to decline economically relative to the West

Qing	1644 – 1911

Rule by Manchurian invaders. Western incursions feebly resisted

Republic of China	1912 – 1949
People's Republic	1949 – present day